METHUEN'S MONOGRAPHS
ON CHEMICAL SUBJECTS

━━━

General Editors: H. J. EMELÉUS, F.R.S
D. W. G. STYLE and R. P. BELL, F.R.S

WAVE MECHANICS
AND VALENCY

WAVE MECHANICS
AND VALENCY

J. W. LINNETT, F.R.S

Fellow of the Queen's College,
Oxford

METHUEN & CO LTD
11 New Fetter Lane London EC4

First published October 13, 1960
Reprinted three times
Reprinted 1970

1.5

© *1960 J. W. Linnett*
Printed in Great Britain
by Butler & Tanner Ltd
Frome and London
SBN 416 40990 3

Distributed in the U.S.A.
by Barnes & Noble Inc.

12/71

To the late J. Ritchie,
my science master

Contents

Illustrations

Preface

The object of this book is to try to explain to the experimental chemist the processes and techniques that are involved in the application of wave mechanics to the electronic structures of atoms and molecules. There are undoubtedly great dangers in the employment of purely qualitative or pictorial wave mechanics; it is much safer to have a surer idea of the principles from which the arguments and pictures are derived. This can only be achieved by examining in some detail a few applications of the basic Schrödinger equation. After all, at school, a fuller understanding of Newton's equation is acquired by personal experience. Likewise it is only possible to achieve any understanding of wave mechanics by personal contact with the equations. In this book an attempt has been made to provide this for the chemist who knows some calculus and has passed Mathematics for Science at A level in the General Certificate of Education. No more should be required.

It is hoped that this book may help a little to remove some of the unfortunate mysticism that has crept into the qualitative presentation and into the jargon of chemical wave mechanics, and also that, in a small way, it may help to reduce some of the unfortunate separation that has occurred between some experimental and theoretical chemists during the last two decades.

Because the book is introductory, much in the last few chapters is left in a very incomplete state. This is inevitable in a short book, but it is hoped that the earlier chapters will have placed the reader in a position to expand his knowledge. At the end of the book there is a list of books and review articles which will help him to do this. No references are included in the text, but, when a person's name appears, a date is given and this should enable the reader to trace the work with the help of the list of books and articles referred to above.

I wish to thank most gratefully R. P. Bell, C. A. Coulson and

E. B. Wilson for reading the first draft of the book and for the time and trouble they took to help me so generously with their advice and experience. My thanks are also due to D. Schofield who carried out the calculation used in Chapter V, Section 4.

I could not conclude this Preface without expressing my very great debt to the wonderful book by L. Pauling and E. B. Wilson and also to the more recent one by W. Kauzmann.

Finally, I wish to thank Mrs Hoare for her assistance in the preparation of this book, and my wife for her encouragement.

CHAPTER I

The Schrödinger Equation

I.1 De Broglie and Schrödinger

In 1924 de Broglie suggested that particles such as electrons might show a dual character, exhibiting the properties of waves as well as those of material particles. By analogy with the behaviour of electromagnetic radiation and photons, he proposed an equation relating the particulate and wave character for a 'particle' not subject to applied forces and moving with constant velocity. This was:

$$mv = \frac{h}{\lambda}, \tag{I.1}$$

where m and v are the mass and velocity of the particle and λ is the wave length of the associated wave; h is Planck's constant. Equation (I.1) relates the particulate behaviour (left-hand side) to the wave behaviour (right-hand side). In this it resembles Planck's equation $E = h\nu$ which summarises the relation between the 'particulate' character of photons and their associated electromagnetic wave behaviour.

The equation for a standing sine wave of wave length λ is:

$$\psi = A . \sin 2\pi \frac{x}{\lambda}, \tag{I.2}$$

where ψ is the value of the quantity whose magnitude is varying in a wave manner, A is the maximum amplitude of this quantity and x is the space coordinate. Double differentiation of I.2 with respect to x gives:

$$\frac{d^2\psi}{dx^2} = -\frac{4\pi^2}{\lambda^2} A . \sin 2\pi \frac{x}{\lambda} = -\frac{4\pi^2}{\lambda^2}\psi. \tag{I.3}$$

From I.1 it follows that the kinetic energy, T, is given by:

$$T = \frac{1}{2}mv^2 = \frac{1}{2m} \cdot \frac{h^2}{\lambda^2}. \tag{I.4}$$

By using I.3 to eliminate λ^2 from I.4:

$$T = -\frac{h^2}{8\pi^2 m} \cdot \frac{1}{\psi} \cdot \frac{d^2\psi}{dx^2}, \tag{I.5}$$

which may be regarded as an alternative form of de Broglie's equation. However, it applies only to a particle moving in a field free space; that is, in a space in which V, the potential energy, is constant, and the particle can be regarded as having only kinetic energy, T. If the potential energy does vary, then the kinetic energy is equal to the difference between the total energy, E, and the potential energy, V:

$$T = E - V. \tag{I.6}$$

Schrödinger (1926) suggested that, for a system which does not change with time, and for which, therefore, the total energy, E, is a constant, I.6 and I.5 could be combined to give:

$$E - V = -\frac{h^2}{8\pi^2 m} \cdot \frac{1}{\psi} \cdot \frac{d^2\psi}{dx^2}. \tag{I.7}$$

This is Schrödinger's equation for one particle in one dimension. It is more usually written as:

$$\frac{d^2\psi}{dx^2} + \frac{8\pi^2 m}{h^2}(E - V)\psi = 0. \tag{I.8}$$

In wave mechanics the expressions used for the potential energy are the same as they would be in classical mechanics. For example, for two charges e_1 and e_2 separated by a distance R, $V = \frac{e_1 . e_2}{R}$. Therefore, as far as energy is concerned, wave mechanics has modified the treatment of kinetic energy but has left that of potential energy unaltered. Further, some results of wave mechanics are fundamentally statistical in character. This will be considered in the next section.

I.2 The Interpretation of ψ

In the last section ψ was referred to vaguely as a 'quantity whose magnitude is varying in a wave manner'. How is this ψ to be defined? With electromagnetic radiation the square of the wave amplitude is interpreted as measuring the radiation intensity, or the photon density. In wave mechanics ψ^2 is interpreted in a corresponding way. However, for systems containing single particles, it is necessary to make the choice between (*a*) regarding ψ^2 as a measure of the 'density of matter', the particle having lost its discrete character, and (*b*) interpreting $\psi^2\,dx$ as a measure of the probability of finding the particle in the length dx between x and $(x + dx)$, thereby retaining the concept of a particle. The latter view has been adopted and ψ^2 is interpreted as measuring a probability.*

Diffraction effects have been observed in experiments with electron beams, the regular pattern of atoms and ions in crystals being used as gratings (Davisson and Germer (1927), and G. P. Thomson (1928)). These confirm the proposition of de Broglie. The diffracted beam can be received on a photographic plate or a scintillation screen. With the latter the arrival of an electron at a point is registered by a flash. The probability of finding electrons at different places on the receiving screen can be calculated using an equation having a wave form (the de Broglie or Schrödinger equations), diffraction effects arising in the usual way. If the experiment is one of long duration, and a photographic plate is used, ψ^2 at a point will be a measure of the blackening of the plate at that point because this depends on the number of electrons arriving. With the scintillation screen ψ^2 will be a measure of the number of flashes per unit area; that is, of the number of electrons. Alternatively, if the experiment were carried out with a single electron, ψ^2 at a given place would measure the probability of observing the arrival of the electron in unit area at that place. The whole behaviour of electrons assumes a statistical character, and it is only possible to state the probability of observing an electron at a particular place. This is a general and essential feature of wave mechanics.

---

* For some problems ψ involves imaginary numbers; that is, $\sqrt{-1}$ (*i*). In these cases ψ^2 is replaced by $\psi\psi^*$ where ψ^* is the complex conjugate of ψ, in which i is replaced by $-i$ in all terms. For example, if $\psi = A \cdot e^{i\phi}$, then $\psi^* = A \cdot e^{-i\phi}$ and $\psi\psi^* = A^2$

I.3 Limitations on ψ

The above interpretation of ψ^2 as a probability places limitations on the solutions that can be allowed for the function ψ, from the Schrödinger equation (I.8). The most important limitations are: *

(i) ψ must be finite for all values of x;
(ii) ψ must be single-valued; that is, for each value of x, ψ must have one value only;
(iii) ψ must be continuous.

All of these are reasonable. As regards (i), if ψ became infinite anywhere, there would be an infinitely greater probability of finding the particle at that point than anywhere else. This would contradict the whole statistical character of wave mechanics and also the Uncertainty Principle of Heisenberg. As regards (ii), if ψ^2 is to be interpreted as a probability, there can clearly only be one value for each value of x. As regards (iii), this appears to be a reasonable requirement for ψ, though it does not follow as necessarily as (i) and (ii) from the probability interpretation of ψ^2. Nevertheless it would be surprising if the probability changed its value discontinuously.

These three requirements *must always* be considered along with and integrally with the Schrödinger equation. Moreover it is because the wave functions ψ are restricted according to (i), (ii) and (iii) that only certain values of E are possible. It is this that leads to the whole concept of quantisation within the framework of wave mechanics. This will be illustrated by the examples treated in the next few chapters. There is no prior proof of either (i), (ii) and (iii) or of the Schrödinger equation or of the interpretation of ψ^2 as a probability. The evidence for them lies in the success attending their application to many problems. There is one further postulate of a kind analogous to (i), (ii) and (iii); namely, the Pauli Principle. This will not be introduced until Chapter VI as the Pauli Principle applies only to systems containing two or more particles, and only single-particle problems are considered before that chapter.

---

* There are special cases where limitation (i) does not apply, but another very similar one replaces it. However, the above will be used here as it is correct for the treatments to be discussed in this book.

I.4 Schrödinger Equation in Three Dimensions

Equations I.4 and I.5 may be written as:

$$\frac{1}{2} \cdot m v_x^2 = - \frac{h^2}{8\pi^2 m} \cdot \frac{1}{\psi} \cdot \frac{\partial^2 \psi}{\partial x^2}, \qquad (I.9)$$

where v_x is the velocity along the x direction. Similar equations may be written for $\frac{1}{2}mv_y^2$ and $\frac{1}{2}mv_z^2$. Combination of these gives:

$$
\begin{aligned}
T &= \tfrac{1}{2}mv_x^2 + \tfrac{1}{2}mv_y^2 + \tfrac{1}{2}mv_z^2 \\
&= - \frac{h^2}{8\pi^2 m} \cdot \frac{1}{\psi} \left\{ \frac{\partial^2 \psi}{\partial x^2} + \frac{\partial^2 \psi}{\partial y^2} + \frac{\partial^2 \psi}{\partial z^2} \right\},
\end{aligned} \qquad (I.10)
$$

so that the Schrödinger equation for a single particle in three dimensions may be written as:

$$\frac{\partial^2 \psi}{\partial x^2} + \frac{\partial^2 \psi}{\partial y^2} + \frac{\partial^2 \psi}{\partial z^2} + \frac{8\pi^2 m}{h^2}(E - V)\psi = 0. \qquad (I.11)$$

For a number of particles a similar sequence of arguments leads to:

$$\frac{1}{m_1}\left\{ \frac{\partial^2 \psi}{\partial x_1^2} + \frac{\partial^2 \psi}{\partial y_1^2} + \frac{\partial^2 \psi}{\partial z_1^2} \right\} + \frac{1}{m_2}\left\{ \frac{\partial^2 \psi}{\partial x_2^2} + \frac{\partial^2 \psi}{\partial y_2^2} + \frac{\partial^2 \psi}{\partial z_2^2} \right\}$$

$$+ \ldots + \frac{8\pi^2}{h^2} \cdot (E - V)\psi = 0, \qquad (I.12)$$

where there are as many differential terms as there are particles; m_1, m_2, etc., are the masses of the particles. It is customary to replace $\left\{ \dfrac{\partial^2 \psi}{\partial x^2} + \dfrac{\partial^2 \psi}{\partial y^2} + \dfrac{\partial^2 \psi}{\partial z^2} \right\}$ by the symbol $\nabla^2 \psi$, so that equation 1.11 is written as:

$$\nabla^2 \psi + \frac{8\pi^2 m}{h^2} \cdot (E - V)\psi = 0. \qquad (I.13)$$

Other forms of nomenclature that are used will be introduced as they become necessary.

B

CHAPTER II

Particle in a Box

II.1 Introduction

The Schrödinger equation will first be applied to a single particle restricted between 0 and L in a single dimension x. This is usually described as *a particle in a one-dimensional box*. One reason for treating this artificial system is its simplicity. Also, it illustrates extremely well the application of the Schrödinger equation and the operation of the limitations (i), (ii) and (iii). It also demonstrates how quantisation, quantum numbers, energy levels and zero point energy arise and introduces the terms: *normalisation* and *orthogonal*. Later in the chapter a single particle in a three-dimensional box will be considered to illustrate the procedure described as 'separation of the wave function', and the phenomenon of degeneracy.

II.2. A Particle in a One-Dimensional Box

Let a particle of mass m be restricted to a line, its position on this line being measured by x. With the particle at positions for which x is less than 0 or greater than L, let the potential energy be infinitely large. Between $x = 0$ and $x = L$ let the potential energy be constant. The energy scale will be chosen so that this potential energy is zero. This may be summarised by: For $x < 0$ and $x > L$, $V = \infty$; for $0 < x < L$, $V = 0$. For the region within the box the Schrödinger equation (I.8) is:

$$\frac{d^2\psi}{dx^2} = -\frac{8\pi^2 mE}{h^2}\psi. \tag{II.1}$$

In this equation $\frac{8\pi^2 mE}{h^2}$ is a constant for a particular value of the energy. It must be positive since E cannot be less than the potential energy of the particle inside the box which is zero. Therefore this equation is satisfied by:

$$\psi = A \sin kx + B \cos kx, \qquad (II.2)$$

where
$$k^2 = \frac{8\pi^2 mE}{h^2}, \qquad (II.3)$$

because double differentiation of II.2 leads to:

$$\frac{d^2\psi}{dx^2} = - k^2 A \sin kx - k^2 B \cos kx$$

$$= - k^2\psi. \qquad (II.4)$$

Equation II.4 is identical with II.1 if II.3 is true. Therefore II.2 is the solution of II.1 if k^2 is given by II.3. At this stage, and as far as satisfying the Schrödinger equation is concerned, k and therefore E can take on any value. The limitation of the solutions arises from the application of the conditions (i) and (iii) of Section I.3.

In the regions in which $V = \infty$, the Schrödinger equation may be written for finite values of E as:

$$\frac{d^2\psi}{dx^2} = + \infty . \psi. \qquad (II.5)$$

Suppose that ψ comes to the edge of the box (at $x = L$) with a finite positive value. Because of condition (iii), ψ will have a positive value at a point for which x is infinitesimally greater than L. But this means that here $\frac{d^2\psi}{dx^2}$ will be infinitely large. Therefore the slope, $\frac{d\psi}{dx}$, will become infinitely large and as a result ψ will rise to infinity. By a similar sequence of arguments, if ψ is negative at $x = L$, ψ will fall immediately to $-\infty$. Both these are disallowed by condition (i) of Section I.3. The only way out of this difficulty is that ψ must be zero at $x = L$ and for all values of x greater than L. Similar arguments require that ψ should be zero at $x = 0$ and for all positions for which x is less than 0. This is moreover consistent with what would be expected, since the particle should not be found in regions where $V = \infty$, consequently ψ^2 and ψ should be zero for such regions.

If ψ is to be zero at $x = 0$, the cosine term must be eliminated from equation II.2 which becomes:

$$\psi = A \sin kx. \tag{II.6}$$

Further, for ψ to be zero at $x = L$:

$$kL = n\pi, \tag{II.7}$$

where $n = 1, 2, 3 \ldots$ or any integer. So equation II.6 becomes:

$$\psi_n = A \sin n\pi \frac{x}{L}, \tag{II.8}$$

where the subscript n has been added to designate the particular solution. Moreover equation II.3 becomes

$$\frac{n^2\pi^2}{L^2} = \frac{8\pi^2 m E_n}{h^2},$$

or

$$E_n = \frac{n^2 h^2}{8mL^2}. \tag{II.9}$$

This gives the energies, E_n, that are possible. This example illustrates how the conditions (i), (ii) and (iii) limit the solutions, and lead to quantised levels. The wave functions given by II.8 for $n = 1, 2$ and 3 are shown in Figure 1.

Because the wave inside the box is a de Broglie sine wave extending over a region in which V is constant this result could have been obtained by a simple application of the de Broglie equation (I.1). The wave length is given by:

$$\lambda = \frac{2L}{n} \tag{II.10}$$

for the state in which an integral number, n, of half-waves fit into the region between 0 and L. The momentum is therefore:

$$mv = \frac{h}{\lambda} = \frac{nh}{2L}, \tag{II.11}$$

and the energy:

$$E_n = \frac{1}{2}mv^2 = \frac{(mv)^2}{2m} = \frac{n^2 h^2}{8mL^2}. \tag{II.12}$$

This is necessarily the same as II.9 since the de Broglie and Schrödinger equations are the same if V is constant.

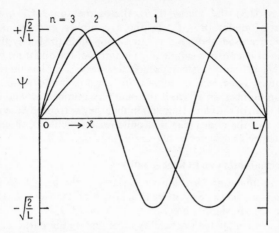

*Fig. 1. Wave functions for three lowest levels of
a particle in a one-dimensional box of length L,
n = 1, 2 and 3*

Reference to Figure 1 shows that, for the lowest or ground state, one half-wave fits into the box; there are no internal nodes. The wave length cannot be longer than this if ψ is to be zero at $x = 0$ and $x = L$, and consequently the energy cannot be smaller than the one corresponding to this wave length; the system cannot have zero energy. This energy of the lowest state is called the zero point energy. The existence of zero point energy is general for systems which involve what would be described classically as a vibratory or to-and-fro motion. As will be seen later, for rotating systems, the rotational energy of the ground state is zero.

For successive energy states the number of nodes increases, being equal to $(n - 1)$ (cf. Figure 1). This type of behaviour is general for all systems. Increasing the number of nodes decreases the 'wave length', which corresponds to increasing the kinetic energy. Many other examples of this will be encountered.

The number n is described as a quantum number. It designates the level and in this case specifies, by simple formulae, the wave function (equation II.8), the energy (II.9), the momentum (II.11), and the number of nodes ($n - 1$). In more complex systems, quantum numbers are used, though it is often impossible to specify the wave function or energy in a simple form in terms of the quantum number. However, in many systems which are very complex the angular momentum does remain related in a very simple manner to a quantum number. In all cases the quantum numbers will convey the general form of the wave function in that they will specify the number and form of the nodes (e.g. in atomic wave functions), though they will not specify the precise algebraic form.

II.3 Normalisation and Orthogonality

The wave functions for the various states of the particle in the box have been shown to be given by II.8. However, the value that is to be given to the constant A has not yet been decided.

For the nth state the probability P_n of finding the particle between x and $x + dx$ is:

$$P_n = \psi_n{}^2 \, dx = A^2 \sin^2 n\pi \frac{x}{L}. dx. \tag{II.13}$$

The integral of this over the whole box must equal unity because there is only one particle and at all times it is somewhere in the box. Therefore

$$\int_0^L \psi_n{}^2 \, dx = \int_0^L A^2 \sin^2 n\pi \frac{x}{L}. dx = 1. \tag{II.14}$$

But

$$\sin^2 n\pi \frac{x}{L} = \frac{1}{2}\left\{1 - \cos 2n\pi \frac{x}{L}\right\}. \tag{II.15}$$

Therefore

$$\int_0^L \psi_n{}^2 \, dx = A^2.\left\{\int_0^L \frac{dx}{2} - \int_0^L \frac{1}{2} \cos 2n\pi \frac{x}{L}. dx\right\}$$

$$= A^2.\left\{\frac{L}{2} - 0\right\} = 1, \tag{II.16}$$

so

$$A = \sqrt{\frac{2}{L}}, \tag{II.17}$$

and the equation (II.8) becomes

$$\psi_n = \sqrt{\frac{2}{L}} \sin n\pi \frac{x}{L}. \tag{II.18}$$

The wave function is now said to be *normalised*. Whereas II.8 on squaring gave relative values of the probabilities, II.18 gives absolute values having regard to the fact that the system contains just one particle. The Schrödinger equation is satisfied whatever the value of A, it is the additional normalisation requirement that serves to fix the constant A for this and for other systems.

Consider the wave functions ψ_n and ψ_m corresponding to two different states of the system (i.e. $n \neq m$). Then it is found that, whatever the values of n and m,

$$\int_0^L \psi_n . \psi_m . dx = 0. \tag{II.19}$$

Functions for which this is true are said to be *orthogonal* to one another, and the wave functions, which are the solutions of the Schrödinger equation for the particle in the box, form an *orthogonal set* (i.e. every member of the set is orthogonal to every other member). It is clear that II.19 is true if n is even and m odd (or vice versa) because then $\psi_n(x) . \psi_m(x) = - \psi_n(L - x) . \psi_m(L - x)$ and, therefore, on integrating II.19, the region on one side of the centre necessarily cancels the region on the other side (cf. with reference to Figure 1, the integral when $n = 2$, $m = 3$). However, II.19 is also true whatever the values of n and m as is shown by the following, it being supposed that $n > m$:

$$\int_0^L \psi_n . \psi_m . dx = \frac{2}{L} \int_0^L \sin n\pi \frac{x}{L} \sin m\pi \frac{x}{L} . dx$$

$$= \frac{1}{L} \int_0^L \left\{ \cos (n - m)\pi \frac{x}{L} - \cos (n + m)\pi \frac{x}{L} \right\} dx$$

$$= \frac{1}{L} \left[\frac{L}{(n - m)\pi} . \sin (n - m)\pi \frac{x}{L} \right.$$
$$\left. - \frac{L}{(n + m)\pi} . \sin (n + m)\pi \frac{x}{L} \right]_0^L$$

$$= 0, \tag{II.20}$$

since $(n - m)$ and $(n + m)$ are integers because n and m are integers. This property of orthogonality ensures that the various wave functions corresponding to the different levels are truly independent of one another. This may be illustrated by the following simple example.

The behaviour of the functions $f_1 = x$ and $f_2 = y$ will be examined,

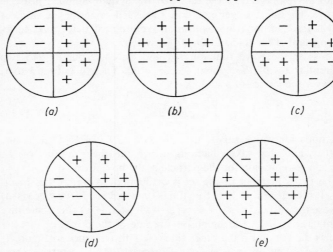

Fig. 2. Diagrammatic illustration of 'orthogonality':

(a) $f_1 = x$; (b) $f_2 = y$; (c) $f_1 f_2 = xy$; (d) $f_3 = \dfrac{1}{\sqrt{2}}(x + y)$;

(e) $f_1 f_3 = x \cdot \dfrac{1}{\sqrt{2}}(x + y)$

using a cartesian coordinate system in two dimensions (x and y), and considering a region of the space limited by a circle of radius r having the origin at the centre. Then f_1 is positive on one side of the y axis and negative on the other (Figure 2a), while f_2 is positive on one side of the x axis and negative on the other (Figure 2b). The product $f_1 f_2 = xy$ has two positive quarters (x and y both positive or both negative) and two negative quarters (x negative and y positive and vice versa) (Figure 2c), and hence the integral over the whole of the space is zero, for these segments are clearly self-cancelling.

Consider, however, the function $f_3 = \frac{1}{\sqrt{2}}(x + y)$. This is zero on

the line $x + y = 0$, positive on one side of it and negative on the

other (Figure 2d). It is clear that the integral of $f_1 f_3 = x \cdot \frac{1}{\sqrt{2}}(x + y)$

over the whole of space is not zero, because the two positive segments exceed the negative segments (Figure 2e). That is, f_1 and f_2 are orthogonal while f_1 and f_3 are not. It is clear that f_3 can be constructed from a combination of the two orthogonal functions f_1 and

$f_2 \left(\frac{1}{\sqrt{2}} f_1 + \frac{1}{\sqrt{2}} f_2 \right)$. That is, f_3 is made up, in part, of f_1. For this

an alternative phrase is: f_1 and f_3 are not orthogonal. But f_1 contains no part of f_2, nor f_2 any part of f_1; they are orthogonal.

When the Schrödinger equation can be solved exactly the wave functions obtained for the different states are, in fact, necessarily orthogonal to one another. That is, they are truly independent of one another. But when approximate solutions have to be used, as is necessary for most chemical problems, thought must be given to the orthogonality of the functions used. Either they must be made orthogonal, or allowance may have to be made for the fact that one of their failings is that they are not orthogonal.

II.4 Particle in a Rectangular Three-Dimensional Box

As in the last example, the potential energy will be set equal to zero for the interior of the box and to infinity for the space outside. Let $V = 0$ for $0 < x < L_x$, $0 < y < L_y$, and $0 < z < L_z$, the box being rectangular. The Schrödinger equation for the region inside the box is:

$$\frac{\partial^2 \psi}{\partial x^2} + \frac{\partial^2 \psi}{\partial y^2} + \frac{\partial^2 \psi}{\partial z^2} + \frac{8\pi^2 m}{h^2} E \cdot \psi = 0. \tag{II.21}$$

Let us test the possibility that the wave function ψ which is a function of x, y, z (i.e. $\psi(x, y, z)$) is a product of three parts separately dependent on x, y and z,

$$\psi(x, y, z) = X(x) \cdot Y(y) \cdot Z(z). \tag{II.22}$$

If this is so then, because $Y(y)$ and $Z(z)$ are independent of x,

$$\frac{\partial^2 \psi}{\partial x^2} = Y.Z.\frac{d^2 X}{dx^2}, \tag{II.23}$$

where X is written in place of $X(x)$. $\frac{\partial^2 \psi}{\partial y^2}$ and $\frac{\partial^2 \psi}{\partial z^2}$ may be treated similarly. Therefore II.21 becomes:

$$YZ.\frac{d^2 X}{dx^2} + XZ.\frac{d^2 Y}{dy^2} + XY.\frac{d^2 Z}{dz^2} + \frac{8\pi^2 mE}{h^2}XYZ = 0. \tag{II.24}$$

Dividing through by $\frac{8\pi^2 m}{h^2}XYZ$, this gives

$$\frac{h^2}{8\pi^2 m}.\frac{1}{X}.\frac{d^2 X}{dx^2} + \frac{h^2}{8\pi^2 m}.\frac{1}{Y}.\frac{d^2 Y}{dy^2} + \frac{h^2}{8\pi^2 m}.\frac{1}{Z}.\frac{d^2 Z}{dz^2} + E = 0. \tag{II.25}$$

The first term is a function of x *only*, the second of y *only* and the third of z *only*. The fourth is a constant. If y and z are kept constant and x varied, the second, third and fourth terms remain constant. Therefore the first term must remain constant. Let this constant be $-_x E$. By a similar argument the second must be constant, say $-_y E$; and likewise the third, at say $-_z E$. We may therefore write

$$\frac{h^2}{8\pi^2 m}.\frac{1}{X}.\frac{d^2 X}{dx^2} = -_x E, \tag{II.26}$$

and similarly for the second and third terms; and also

$$_x E + {}_y E + {}_z E = E. \tag{II.27}$$

The substitution II.22 is satisfactory because, by *separating* ψ into a product of three independent parts, separated equations such as II.26 can be obtained. Equation II.26 is identical with II.1, so that

$$X(x) = \sqrt{\frac{2}{L_x}}\sin n_x \pi \frac{x}{L_x}, \tag{II.28}$$

there being similar solutions for $Y(y)$ and $Z(z)$ which involve the quantum numbers n_y and n_z. Further

$$_x E_{n_x} = \frac{n_x^2 h^2}{8mL_x^2}, \tag{II.29}$$

and there are analogous expressions for $_y E_{n_y}$ and $_z E_{n_z}$. The total energy is, from II.27,

$$E_{n_x.n_y.n_z} = \frac{h^2}{8m}\left\{\frac{n_x^2}{L_x^2} + \frac{n_y^2}{L_y^2} + \frac{n_z^2}{L_z^2}\right\}. \quad \text{(II.30)}$$

Because the problem is a three-dimensional one, there are three quantum numbers n_x, n_y and n_z. In this particular example these specify the momenta and energies associated with the three cartesian coordinates, x, y and z. They also specify the total wave function which is

$$\psi_{n_x.n_y.n_z} = \sqrt{\frac{8}{L_x.L_y.L_z}}.\sin n_x\pi\,\frac{x}{L_x}.\sin n_y\pi\,\frac{y}{L_y}.\sin n_z\pi\,\frac{z}{L_z}. \quad \text{(II.31)}$$

These functions can be visualised by reference to Figure 1.

In other systems the same features are found. For instance with the hydrogen atom there are three quantum numbers associated with the spatial position of the electron. These are linked to the angular momentum, its orientation and the energy. In more complex examples, the connection between quantum numbers and particular properties does not remain so close but, as stated earlier, electronic angular momentum is quantised in an extremely simple manner in a wide variety of systems.

II.5 Particle in a Cubic Box

For a cubic box, $L_x = L_y = L_z = L$. Thus

$$E_{n_x.n_y.n_z} = \frac{h^2}{8mL^2}\{n_x^2 + n_y^2 + n_z^2\}. \quad \text{(II.32)}$$

The energies of the more low-lying states are shown in Figure 3. The zero point energy is three times that for a one-dimensional box, there being a part associated with each of the three coordinates. Secondly, for the level for which the energy is $6\frac{h^2}{8mL^2}$, there are three independent states having the quantum numbers (2, 1, 1), (1, 2, 1) and (1, 1, 2) for (n_x, n_y, n_z). This level is said to be *three-fold degenerate* or *triply degenerate*. The level for which the energy is $14\frac{h^2}{8mL^2}$ is six-fold degenerate, being made up of states for which the quantum numbers are (3, 2, 1), (3, 1, 2), (2, 1, 3), (2, 3. 1), (1, 2, 3) and

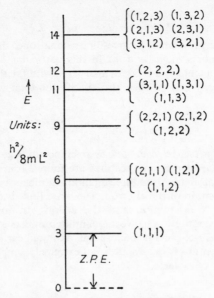

Fig. 3. Energy levels of particle in a cubic box of side L illustrating degeneracy and zero point energy (Z.P.E.)

(1, 3, 2). On the other hand, the ground state and several others are *non-degenerate*.

The wave functions for the three members of the above triply degenerate level, having $E = 6\dfrac{h^2}{8mL^2}$, are different. One has a nodal plane at $x = \dfrac{L}{2}$, another a nodal plane at $y = \dfrac{L}{2}$, and the third a nodal plane at $z = \dfrac{L}{2}$. Suppose that a slight distortion were applied to the cube. For example, suppose that the x dimension were increased by a small amount ∂L. Then the change in energy of the first state which has $4\dfrac{h^2}{8mL^2}$ associated with the x direction will be different from the change for the other two states which have $\dfrac{h^2}{8mL^2}$ associated with the x direction. To a first approximation the decrease in energy for the first state will be $\dfrac{8\partial L}{L} \cdot \dfrac{h^2}{8mL^2}$, whereas that for the other two will only be $\dfrac{2\partial L}{L} \cdot \dfrac{h^2}{8mL^2}$. Such breakdowns of the degeneracy, which occur on applying a small modification to the system, are often observed in practice. For example, many atomic states are degenerate but, when a magnetic or electric field is applied, the degenerate level breaks up into several separate levels, so that spectral lines which were single become multiplets.

Conclusion

This chapter has shown how quantisation into energy levels arises. The spacing between the levels is greater the smaller the mass of the particle, and the smaller the box. As regards the latter, the wave lengths are reduced and hence the energies are increased. The momentum is quantised independently of the mass of the particle but because the energy is given by $\dfrac{1}{2m}(mv)^2$ the energies are greater the smaller the mass. The way in which the energy increases with an increasing number of nodes in the wave function has also been demonstrated. This is a general feature when problems are treated by wave mechanics.

CHAPTER III

Particle in a Ring and on a Sphere

═══

III.1 Introduction

The object of this chapter is to examine the quantisation of angular momentum. The reason for doing this is that the quantisation of the angular momentum of electrons is extremely important in its effect on their spatial distribution, and on spectroscopic and other properties of atoms and molecules.

III.2 Particle in a Ring

Let a particle of mass m be restricted to a circular line of radius r, on which the potential energy is constant. The angular coordinate ϕ will be used. It can vary from 0 to 2π radians (0 to 360°). The Schrödinger equation, appropriate to this problem, is

$$\frac{1}{r^2} \cdot \frac{d^2\psi}{d\phi^2} + \frac{8\pi^2 m}{h^2}(E - V)\psi = 0. \tag{III.1}$$

This is derived in Appendix I.

The potential energy will be set equal to zero so that III.1 becomes

$$\frac{d^2\psi}{d\phi^2} + \frac{8\pi^2 mr^2}{h^2}E\psi = 0. \tag{III.2}$$

Solutions of this are

$$\psi_{sM} = N_M . \sin M\phi \tag{III.3}$$

and

$$\psi_{cM} = N_M . \cos M\phi, \tag{III.4}$$

where

$$M^2 = \frac{8\pi^2 mr^2}{h^2}E, \tag{III.5}$$

and N_M is a normalising constant.

How do the conditions (i), (ii) and (iii) restrict the solutions in this

example? In III.3 and 4, ψ is finite whatever the value of ϕ, so that
(i) is satisfied. In Figure 4 two solutions of III.2, the sine functions
corresponding to two values of M, are shown. Now the coordinate ϕ is repetitive, $\phi = 2\pi$ corresponding to the same point as
$\phi = 0$, and $(2\pi + \phi)$ to the same point as ϕ. Therefore, if the function is to be both single-valued and continuous, $\psi(\phi)$ must equal
$\psi(2\pi + \phi)$. This can only be true if M is an integer. Reference to

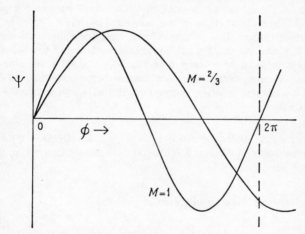

Fig. 4. Graphs of sin $M\theta$ *for* $M = \frac{2}{3}$ *and* 1 *showing that*
$M = 1$ *is acceptable while* $M = \frac{2}{3}$ *is not*

Figure 4 shows that, if it is not, there will either be a discontinuity
at $\phi = 2\pi$, or the function will not be single-valued.

It is necessary to consider why $\psi = N \sin \frac{1}{2}\phi$ is not satisfactory
because this satisfies the condition that $\psi(0) = \psi(2\pi)$. However, for
this function, there would be a discontinuity in the gradient at
$\phi = 0$ (or 2π). With the particle in the box there was a discontinuity
in the slope at the edge of the box but, at that point, there was
a discontinuity in the potential energy. In such an artificial situation,
while ψ does not change discontinuously, $\frac{d\psi}{dx}$ does. However, where

there is no discontinuity in V as is the case in all real systems both ψ and $\frac{d\psi}{dx}$ must be continuous. Therefore solutions such as $N \sin \frac{1}{2}\phi$, $N \sin \frac{3}{2}\phi$, etc., are not satisfactory.

The energy levels are therefore given by

$$E_M = \frac{M^2h^2}{8\pi^2mr^2} = \frac{M^2h^2}{8\pi^2I},$$ (III.6)

where I is the moment of inertia, mr^2. This result may be compared with that for the particle in the box (cf. II.9). They differ in one important respect. In this case M can have the value zero as well as 1, 2, 3, etc. When M is not equal to zero there are two solutions for each value of M corresponding to III.3 and III.4, the sine and cosine solutions. Such states are doubly degenerate. For $M = 0$, there is only one solution corresponding to III.4 (since $\sin 0 = 0$). This solution is

$$\psi_0 = \text{a constant } (N_0).$$ (III.7)

These results can be obtained by applying de Broglie's equation which can be used because V is constant. The wave length, λ, must be

$$\lambda = \frac{2\pi r}{M}.$$ (III.8)

Therefore, the linear momentum is given by

$$mv = \frac{h}{\lambda} = \frac{Mh}{2\pi r},$$ (III.9)

and the energy by

$$E_M = \frac{(mv)^2}{2m} = \frac{M^2h^2}{8\pi^2mr^2}$$ (III.10)

which is identical with III.6. The angular momentum $I\omega$, where ω is the angular velocity and is equal to $\frac{v}{r}$, is given by

$$I\omega = (mr^2)\left(\frac{v}{r}\right) = mvr = M\frac{h}{2\pi}.$$ (III.11)

The angular momentum is quantised in units of $\frac{h}{2\pi}$. The case of $M = 0$ corresponds, in the de Broglie approach, to an infinite wave length, there being no variation of ψ round the ring, and the angular momentum is zero.

Because a state having $M = 0$ (for which $E = 0$) is possible, there is no zero point energy in systems of this kind. That is, zero point energy is not encountered for motions along coordinates for which the P.E. remains constant (e.g. rotations) while it does appear for motions for which the P.E. varies with the coordinate (e.g. vibrations). In both cases the zero of the energy scale is at the minimum energy possible and, relative to this, the 'zero-point-energy' is zero for a rotation and finite for a vibration.

It is apparent, from the calculations of this section, that angular momentum will be quantised in the simple way found here in many systems. If in any system there is rotational symmetry such that the potential energy does not change round a circular track, then the angular part of the wave function must be identical with that which has just been discussed. In particular, the necessity of fitting an integral number of waves between 0 and 2π results in the angular momentum being quantised according to III.49 (cf. the hydrogen atom in the next chapter). This situation is found, for example, in diatomic molecules where V is constant along circles round the molecular axis. As a result the angular momentum about this axis is quantised in units of $\frac{h}{2\pi}$. In diatomic molecules, wave functions for which the angular momentum is zero are described as σ 'orbitals', those for which it is $\frac{h}{2\pi}$ as π 'orbitals', and those for which it is $2\frac{h}{2\pi}$ as δ 'orbitals'.

The normalisation constants in III.3 and III.4 can be found by the procedure described in Section II.3. It is found that $N_0 = \frac{1}{\sqrt{2\pi}}$ and that $N_1 = N_2 = N_3 = \ldots = \frac{1}{\sqrt{\pi}}$.

III.3 Alternative Solutions

The two solutions $\frac{1}{\sqrt{\pi}}.\sin M\phi$ and $\frac{1}{\sqrt{\pi}}.\cos M\phi$ are orthogonal

c

because $\int_0^{2\pi} \dfrac{1}{\sqrt{\pi}} \sin M\phi . \dfrac{1}{\sqrt{\pi}}.\cos M\phi . d\phi$

$$= \frac{1}{2\pi} \int_0^{2\pi} \sin 2M\phi . d\phi$$

$$= \frac{1}{2\pi} \left[-\frac{1}{2M} \cos 2M\phi \right]_0^{2\pi} = 0. \qquad \text{(III.12)}$$

They are therefore independent solutions corresponding to the same energy.

However, let us test a solution which is a combination of them, namely

$$\psi = a \frac{1}{\sqrt{\pi}}.\sin M\phi + b \frac{1}{\sqrt{\pi}}.\cos M\phi. \qquad \text{(III.13)}$$

Double differentiation of this gives

$$\frac{d^2\psi}{d\phi^2} = -M^2 a \frac{1}{\sqrt{\pi}} \sin M\phi - M^2 b \frac{1}{\sqrt{\pi}} \cos M\phi$$

$$= -M^2\psi. \qquad \text{(III.14)}$$

Reference to III.3 and to III.5 shows that this is identical with the behaviour of the original functions III.3 and III.4 and therefore III.13 is equally satisfactory as a solution of the Schrödinger equation. Moreover, this is true whatever the values of a and b. Normalisation requirements provide a relationship between a and b:

$$\int_0^{2\pi} \left(a \frac{1}{\sqrt{\pi}}.\sin M\phi + b \frac{1}{\sqrt{\pi}}.\cos M\phi \right)^2 d\phi$$

$$= a^2 \int_0^{2\pi} \frac{1}{\pi} \sin^2 M\phi \, d\phi + b^2 \int_0^{2\pi} \frac{1}{\pi} \cos^2 M\phi \, d\phi$$

$$+ 2ab \int_0^{2\pi} \frac{1}{\pi} \sin M\phi \cos M\phi \, d\phi$$

$$= a^2 + b^2 = 1, \qquad \text{(III.15)}$$

use having been made of the normalisation and orthogonality of the basic functions. The simplest way of representing a and b to satisfy III.15 is to put

$$a = \cos \alpha \quad \text{and} \quad b = \sin \alpha \qquad \text{(III.16)}$$

where α can have any value.

Therefore the solution

$$\psi = \frac{\cos\alpha}{\sqrt{\pi}}.\sin M\phi + \frac{\sin\alpha}{\sqrt{\pi}}.\cos M\phi \qquad \text{(III.17)}$$

satisfies the Schrödinger equation and is normalised. However, this function is no longer orthogonal to the original functions III.3 or III.4. It is easy to demonstrate that it is orthogonal to

$$\psi = -\frac{\sin\alpha}{\sqrt{\pi}}.\sin M\phi + \frac{\cos\alpha}{\sqrt{\pi}}\cos M\phi. \qquad \text{(III.18)}$$

Moreover III.18 is normalised also. Therefore the new orthogonal pair III.17 and III.18 can replace the original pair III.3 and III.4. The pair III.17 and III.18 may be written alternatively as

$$\psi = \frac{1}{\sqrt{\pi}}\sin(M\phi + \alpha)$$

and

$$\psi = \frac{1}{\sqrt{\pi}}\cos(M\phi + \alpha). \qquad \text{(III.19)}$$

The change corresponds, in this case, to moving the origin round the circle and it is clear that, corresponding to the energy E_M, there will be an infinite number of degenerate pairs, which will satisfy the Schrödinger equation. However, the selection of one member of the pair defines the other by the orthogonality requirement.

III.4 Properties of a System in Wave Mechanics

In wave mechanics, the properties of a system are of two kinds: those that have a definite value independent of the position of the particle or particles, and those which vary with the value of the coordinate. For example, in the problems considered so far, the value of E, the energy, is independent of the position and is therefore sharply defined. On the other hand, it is only possible to give a probability function for the position.

In Chapter I, it was found that, for the particle in field free space, the kinetic energy was given by

$$\frac{1}{\psi}\left\{-\frac{h^2}{8\pi^2 m}.\frac{d^2}{dx^2}(\psi)\right\} = T. \qquad \text{(III.20)}$$

In this case, T is a quantity that is constant and independent of x. But, when the potential energy is not constant over the region considered,

$$\frac{1}{\psi}\left\{-\frac{h^2}{8\pi^2 m}\cdot\frac{d^2}{dx^2}(\psi)\right\} = T = E - V, \qquad \text{(III.21)}$$

and T is not constant but varies with x.

It is a *postulate* of wave mechanics that any property, which has a definite value for a given state and does not vary with the coordinate or coordinates, can be calculated by this type of procedure. For any property, there is an operator, A, and if

$$\frac{1}{\psi}\{A\psi\} = \text{a constant}, \qquad \text{(III.22)}$$

then that property has a definite value given by equation III.22 and equal to the constant.

What is an *operator*? It will be described by examples. The differentials $\frac{d}{dx}$ and $\frac{d^2}{dx^2}$ are *operators* because they symbolise the carrying out of well-defined *operations* on the function that follows them $\left(\text{e.g. } \frac{d}{dx}(x^n) = nx^{n-1}\right)$. By comparing III.20 and III.22 it is clear that the operator that will give the kinetic energy along the x-coordinate is $-\frac{h^2}{8\pi^2 m}\cdot\frac{d^2}{dx^2}$.

In this chapter we are concerned with momentum. What operator is to be used in III.22 for obtaining the momentum? The answer is obtained by comparing the classical expression for the kinetic energy $\left(\frac{p^2}{2m} \text{ where } p \text{ is the momentum}\right)$ with the above operator for the same quantity. It follows that the operator for the momentum must be $\frac{h}{2\pi i}\cdot\frac{d}{dx}$ where $i = \sqrt{-1}$. The operator for the square of the momentum would be $-\frac{h^2}{4\pi^2}\cdot\frac{d^2}{dx^2}$. Since the distance along a circular orbit is given by $r\cdot\phi$, the operator for the *angular* momentum about the defined axis, which is r times the linear momentum along the orbit (cf. III.11), is $\frac{h}{2\pi i} \cdot \frac{d}{d\phi}$ and the operator for the square of this angular momentum is $-\frac{h^2}{4\pi^2} \cdot \frac{d^2}{d\phi^2}$.

Applying III.22 to III.3 we obtain, for the angular momentum of the particle in the system considered in the second section of this chapter,

$$\frac{1}{N_M . \sin M\phi} \left\{ \frac{h}{2\pi i} \cdot \frac{d}{d\phi}(N_M . \sin M\phi) \right\} = \frac{Mh}{2\pi i} \cot M\phi, \quad \text{(III.23)}$$

and for the square of the angular momentum

$$\frac{1}{N_M . \sin M\phi} \left\{ -\frac{h^2}{4\pi^2} \cdot \frac{d^2}{d\phi^2}(N_M . \sin M\phi) \right\} = M^2 . \frac{h^2}{4\pi^2}. \quad \text{(III.24)}$$

The square of the angular momentum is independent of x and definite but the angular momentum itself is not, for the R.H.S. of III.23 is not a constant. The same would be found for the cosine solution III.4, the square of the angular momentum being the same as in III.24. Therefore the result III.11, derived by applying de Broglie's relation, is a little misleading. Because p^2 is defined, it would appear that the absolute value of the angular momentum is defined, and is equal to $M\frac{h}{2\pi}$, but that its sign or direction is not defined for either III.3 or III.4. In the next section the solutions of III.2, which do not suffer from this difficulty, will be derived and examined.

III.5 Further Alternative Solutions

The Schrödinger equation III.2 is also satisfied by the functions

$$\psi_M = N'_M . e^{iM\phi} \quad \text{(III.25)}$$

and

$$\psi_M = N'_M . e^{-iM\phi} \quad \text{(III.26)}$$

where i is $\sqrt{-1}$. Double differentiation of these shows that they correspond to the energies given by III.5. These solutions could have been derived by a procedure somewhat similar to that used in III.3 because

$$\sin M\phi = \frac{1}{2i}\{e^{iM\phi} - e^{-iM\phi}\}$$

and
$$\cos M\phi = \frac{1}{2}\{e^{iM\phi} + e^{-iM\phi}\}, \tag{III.27}$$

therefore
$$e^{iM\phi} = \cos M\phi + i\sin M\phi$$

and
$$e^{-iM\phi} = \cos M\phi - i\sin M\phi. \tag{III.28}$$

Because of the relation to the sine and cosine functions expressed in III.28, M must be integral in order that the function shall be single-valued.

Because the functions are imaginary, the probability is given by
$$\psi_M . \psi_M{}^* = N'_M . e^{iM\phi} . N'_M . e^{-iM\phi} = (N'_M)^2. \tag{III.29}$$

That is, these functions (for the above is true for both III.25 and III.26) lead to a constant probability round the ring. This is more satisfactory, since no particular direction in the ring has any special significance. Equation III.29 shows that
$$N'_M = \frac{1}{\sqrt{2\pi}} \tag{III.30}$$

for all values of M.

Using the postulate of the last section, the angular momentum is given, for one state, by
$$\frac{1}{\frac{1}{\sqrt{2\pi}} . e^{iM\phi}}\left\{\frac{h}{2\pi i} . \frac{d}{d\phi}\left(\frac{1}{\sqrt{2\pi}} . e^{iM\phi}\right)\right\} = M\frac{h}{2\pi}, \tag{III.31}$$

and, for the other state, by
$$\frac{1}{\frac{1}{\sqrt{2\pi}} . e^{-iM\phi}}\left\{\frac{h}{2\pi i} . \frac{d}{d\phi}\left(\frac{1}{\sqrt{2\pi}} . e^{-iM\phi}\right)\right\} = -M\frac{h}{2\pi}. \tag{III.32}$$

Therefore for III.25 and III.26 the angular momenta have values independent of ϕ. For one, it has a positive sign, and for the other, a negative sign.

For a particle restricted to a circle there are two sets of solutions therefore. The real set, which are
$$\psi_0 = \frac{1}{\sqrt{2\pi}}$$

and $\qquad \psi_M = \dfrac{1}{\sqrt{\pi}}.\sin M\phi \quad$ and $\quad \dfrac{1}{\sqrt{\pi}}\cos M\phi;$ (III.33)

and the imaginary set

$$\psi_0 = \frac{1}{\sqrt{2\pi}}$$

and $\qquad \psi_M = \dfrac{1}{\sqrt{2\pi}}e^{iM\phi} \quad$ and $\quad \dfrac{1}{\sqrt{2\pi}}e^{-iM\phi}.$ (III.34)

As regards the latter, because the associated angular momenta are $+M\dfrac{h}{2\pi}$ and $-M\dfrac{h}{2\pi}$, we may say that the quantum number can have the values $+M$ or $-M$, the former corresponding to $\dfrac{1}{\sqrt{2\pi}}e^{iM\phi}$ and the latter to $\dfrac{1}{\sqrt{2\pi}}e^{-iM\phi}.$

The imaginary solutions are, in some ways, to be preferred because they correspond to well-defined values of the momenta; and because a uniform distribution of the particle round the ring is more reasonable. On the other hand, the real functions (III.3 and III.4) have the advantage that they can be visualised and represented graphically.

III.6 Particle on the Surface of a Sphere

Positions on the surface of a sphere may be specified by the method used for the earth's surface, using latitude and longitude. The coordinate θ will be used to measure 'latitude' but will run from 0° at the 'north pole' through 90° $\left(\dfrac{\pi}{2}\right)$ at the 'equator' to 180° (π) at the 'south pole'. The line through the poles will be regarded as the z axis, the equator lying in the xy plane. The coordinate ϕ will be used to measure 'longitude' but will run from 0° where the xz plane cuts the sphere round to 360° (2π).

For a particle restricted to the surface of a sphere of radius r, the Schrödinger equation, in terms of the coordinate θ and ϕ, is

$$\frac{1}{r^2}.\frac{\partial^2\psi}{\partial\theta^2} + \frac{\cos\theta}{r^2\sin\theta}.\frac{\partial\psi}{\partial\theta} + \frac{1}{r^2\sin^2\theta}.\frac{\partial^2\psi}{\partial\phi^2} + \frac{8\pi^2 m}{h^2}(E - V)\psi = 0. \quad \text{(III.35)}$$

This can be derived by a procedure similar to that used in Appendix I. The potential energy will be assumed to be uniform and equal to zero. Let us test the possibility that the wave function ψ can be separated as follows:

$$\psi(\theta, \phi) = \Theta(\theta) . \Phi(\phi). \qquad \text{(III.36)}$$

Substitution of this in III.35 gives, after rearranging:

$$\sin^2 \theta \frac{1}{\Theta} . \frac{d^2\Theta}{d\theta^2} + \sin \theta \cos \theta \frac{1}{\Theta} . \frac{d\Theta}{d\theta} + \frac{1}{\Phi} . \frac{d^2\Phi}{d\phi^2} + \frac{8\pi^2 m r^2 \sin^2 \theta E}{h^2} = 0. \qquad \text{(III.37)}$$

The first, second and fourth terms are dependent on θ only, the third is dependent on ϕ only. Therefore, as before, it follows that

$$\frac{1}{\Phi} . \frac{d^2\Phi}{d\phi^2} = \text{a constant.} \qquad \text{(III.38)}$$

This is identical with III.2. The solutions are either the real set III.33 or the imaginary set III.34. In either event, the constant in III.38 is equal to $-M^2$. The equation for Θ, derived from III.37, is

$$\frac{d^2\Theta}{d\theta^2} + \frac{\cos \theta}{\sin \theta} . \frac{d\Theta}{d\theta} - \frac{M^2}{\sin^2 \theta}\Theta + \beta\Theta = 0, \qquad \text{(III.39)}$$

where

$$\beta = \frac{8\pi^2 m r^2 E}{h^2}. \qquad \text{(III.40)}$$

This situation is different from that for the three-dimensional box, where the solutions for the separated functions were completely independent of one another. In this case, the solution for Θ is dependent on M, which means that it is dependent on the function Φ which is the solution of III.38.

If $M = 0$, III.39 becomes

$$\frac{d^2\Theta}{d\theta^2} + \frac{\cos \theta}{\sin \theta} . \frac{d\Theta}{d\theta} + \beta\Theta = 0. \qquad \text{(III.41)}$$

To solve this equation in a logical way requires a rather lengthy argument,* so the results will be listed and can be tested by sub-

* The argument is analogous in many ways to the example given in Section 2 of the next chapter.

stitution in the III.41. The simplest solution is

$$\Theta_0 = \text{a constant.} \tag{III.42}$$

This is true if $\beta = 0$. Further solutions involving increasing values of β are

$$\Theta_1 = N_1 \cos \theta \qquad \text{if } \beta = 2 \tag{III.43}$$

$$\Theta_2 = N_2(3 \cos^2 \theta - 1) \qquad \text{if } \beta = 6 \tag{III.44}$$

$$\Theta_3 = N_3(\tfrac{5}{3} \cos^3 \theta - \cos \theta) \text{ if } \beta = 12. \tag{III.45}$$

The functions are numbered successively, the number being that of the highest power of $\cos \theta$ in the function. If this number is l, it can be seen that

$$\beta = l(l + 1). \tag{III.46}$$

Therefore the energies of successive levels are:

$$E_l = \frac{h^2}{8\pi^2 mr^2} l(l + 1)$$

$$= \frac{h^2}{8\pi^2 I} l(l + 1), \tag{III.47}$$

where I is the moment of inertia, mr^2.* Since E is given by

$$E = \frac{(p_{\text{ang}})^2}{2I} \tag{III.48}$$

where p_{ang} is the total angular momentum, it follows that the square of this quantity is equal to

$$l(l + 1)\left[\frac{h}{2\pi}\right]^2. \tag{III.49}$$

For the general case in which $M \neq 0$, the solutions are of the form

$$\Theta = \sin^{|M|} \theta . f(\cos \theta), \tag{III.50}$$

where $f(\cos \theta)$ represents polynomials in $\cos \theta$ similar though not identical with III.42 to III.45 and $|M|$ is the absolute value of M.† The functions $f(\cos \theta)$ for $|M| = 0$, 1 and 2 are listed in Table I,

---

* Formula III.47 is that for the rotational energy levels of a rigid diatomic or linear molecule; this is so because the Schrödinger equation takes on the same form when applied to that system as when applied to the present one.

† The symbol $|M|$ means 'the absolute value of M'; that is, the value without regard to sign. The absolute value of $+6$ and -6 is 6.

which also gives the values of β necessary for III.39 to be satisfied. In this Table normalising constants have been omitted. From Table I it is apparent that β is given by III.46 even when $M \neq 0$. That is, the energy is given in general by III.47 and the square of the total angular momentum by III.49.

There is, however, a limitation on the value of l which is demonstrated by Table I; it is that l cannot be less than M. This may be put in another way. For a given energy level (i.e. for a given value of l), $| M |$ can have any integral value from 0 to l. Or alternatively M can have any integral value from $-l$ to $+l$ (see the last section). Therefore the energy levels have a degeneracy given by $(2l + 1)$.

TABLE I

$\| M \| = 0$		$\| M \| = 1$		$\| M \| = 2$	
$f(\cos \theta)$	β	$f(\cos \theta)$	β	$f(\cos \theta)$	β
1	0	1	2	1	6
$\cos \theta$	2	$\cos \theta$	6	$\cos \theta$	12
$3 \cos^2 \theta - 1$	6	$5 \cos^2 \theta - 1$	12	$7 \cos^2 \theta - 1$	20
$\frac{5}{3} \cos^3 \theta - \cos \theta$	12	$\frac{7}{3} \cos^3 \theta - \cos \theta$	20	$\frac{9}{3} \cos^3 \theta - \cos \theta$	30

The total angular momentum for the energy level defined by l may be regarded as having the magnitude $\sqrt{l(l + 1)} . \frac{h}{2\pi}$. The angular momentum about the axis selected as an axis of reference is also quantised. The values this can have are $M \frac{h}{2\pi}$, M having any integral value from $-l$ to $+l$. Therefore, even at its maximum, the angular momentum about the reference axis is less than the total angular momentum, though the difference between the two decreases as l increases. Because this problem is a two-dimensional one, two quantum numbers, l and M, are required (cf. Chapter II.4), which define respectively the total angular momentum and the energy (l) and the resolved part of the angular momentum about a particular axis (M).

III.7 The Form of the Wave Functions

In this section, the solutions for Φ will be used in their real form, though some reference will be made to $\psi\psi^*$, the probability, for the imaginary solutions. Normalising constants will be omitted.

For $l = 0$ and $M = 0$, the wave function is constant over the surface of the sphere.

For $l = 1$, there are three functions:

$$\text{for} \quad M = 0 \qquad \psi = \cos \theta, \tag{III.51}$$

$$\text{for} \ |M| = 1 \qquad \psi = \sin \theta . \sin \phi \tag{III.52}$$

$$\text{and} \ \sin \theta . \cos \phi. \tag{III.53}$$

The first has its largest positive value in the $+z$ direction and a negative value of the same magnitude in the $-z$ direction. ψ is zero for $\theta = \dfrac{\pi}{2}$; that is, the xy plane is a nodal plane. On one side of the xy plane, ψ is positive, and, on the other, negative. The other two functions (III.52 and III.53) are similar in form, though differently oriented, the former having the xz plane and the latter the yz plane as a nodal plane. This triply degenerate set is entirely analogous to the atomic wave functions described by the letter p (representing $l = 1$). The set is also similar to the triply degenerate set that was discussed for a particle in a cubic box.

For $l = 2$, there are five functions:

$$\text{for} \quad M = 0 \qquad \psi = 3 \cos^2 \theta - 1, \tag{III.54}$$

$$\text{for} \ |M| = 1 \qquad \psi = \sin \theta \cos \theta . \sin \phi \tag{III.55}$$

$$\text{and} \ \sin \theta \cos \theta . \cos \phi, \tag{III.56}$$

$$\text{for} \ |M| = 2 \qquad \psi = \sin^2 \theta . \sin 2\phi \tag{III.57}$$

$$\text{and} \ \sin^2 \theta . \cos 2\phi. \tag{III.58}$$

The first has its largest positive value in the $+z$ and $-z$ directions. In the xy plane it is negative, the absolute value being half that in the $+z$ and $-z$ directions.

Between these are two circular nodal lines. For one $\cos \theta = \dfrac{1}{\sqrt{3}}$ ($\theta = 54\frac{3}{4}°$) and for the other $\cos \theta = -\dfrac{1}{\sqrt{3}}$ ($\theta = 125\frac{1}{4}°$). For III.55,

ψ is zero for $\theta = 0$ and $180°$, for $\theta = 90°$ and for $\phi = 0$ and $180°$. There are therefore nodal lines where the xy and xz planes cut the sphere. The maximum positive values are at $\theta = 45°$, $\phi = 90°$; and $\theta = 135°$, $\phi = 270°$, and the maximum negative values at $\theta = 45°$, $\phi = 270°$; and $\theta = 135°$, $\phi = 90°$. III.56 is similar except that the two nodal lines lie in the xy and yz planes. III.57 is also similar, the two nodal lines being in the xz ($\phi = 0$ and $180°$) and the yz ($\phi = 90$ and $270°$) planes. III.58 is similar in form to the other three but the two nodal lines are at $\phi = 45°$ and $225°$; and $\phi = 135°$ and $315°$. Therefore III.55 to 58 are all similar in form but differently oriented. These wave functions are analogous to the atomic set described by the letter d ($l = 2$).

The function for $l = 0$ has no nodal lines, those for $l = 1$ have one and those for $l = 2$ have two. The number of nodal lines is equal to l. An attempt is made to represent the three p and five d functions diagrammatically in Figure 5. This has been done by plotting contour diagrams on a plane projection of the surface of a sphere. Mollweide's elliptical projection has been used (as in Geography). It is easy to see the correspondence between the more common representation of the p and d atomic orbitals and the present one.

If the imaginary solutions are used for the Φ function it would only be possible to represent graphically the probability $\psi\psi^*$. The formulae are listed below for the p and d states and could be represented graphically in a manner similar to that used in Figure 5. As before, normalisation constants have been omitted.

$$l = 1 \quad M = 0 \quad \psi\psi^* = \cos^2\theta$$
$$l = 1 \quad M = \pm 1 \quad \psi\psi^* = \sin^2\theta$$
$$l = 2 \quad M = 0 \quad \psi\psi^* = (3\cos^2\theta - 1)^2$$
$$l = 2 \quad M = \pm 1 \quad \psi\psi^* = \sin^2\theta\cos^2\theta$$
$$l = 2 \quad M = \pm 2 \quad \psi\psi^* = \sin^4\theta.$$

In all cases $\psi\psi^*$ is independent of ϕ.

III.8 Conclusion

In this chapter, the way in which the conditions (i), (ii) and (iii) limit the solution of the Schrödinger equation for a particle on a circle and the surface of a sphere has been described. One important result

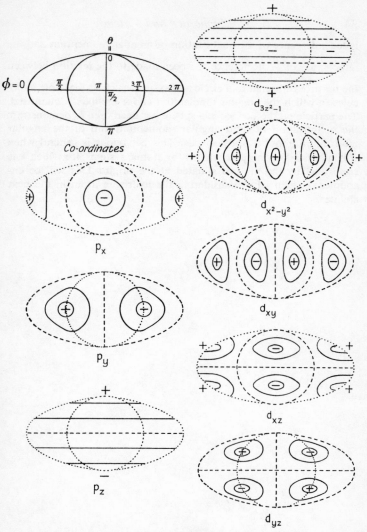

Fig. 5. Contour diagrams of the three p and five d functions for a particle on the surface of a sphere, an elliptical projection of the surface being used (Mollweide's). Contours are shown by full lines, nodes by broken lines, and other necessary coordinates by dotted lines

is the emergence of the quantisation of angular momentum and the importance of $\frac{h}{2\pi}$. Reference has been made to the relation between the particle restricted to a circle and systems such as diatomic molecules in which the angular momentum about the axis is quantised. The particle on the surface of a sphere has been used to demonstrate the quantisation of total angular momentum and of the angular momentum about a selected axis. This behaviour is general when V is spherically symmetric; that is for atomic systems, for which V is controlled by the nucleus situated at the origin. This will be encountered again when considering the hydrogen atom in the next chapter.

CHAPTER IV

The Hydrogen Atom

IV.1 Introduction

The Schrödinger equation will now be applied to a system that exists, namely the hydrogen atom. The complete solution is lengthy so, to begin with, only the wave functions which are spherically symmetrical will be considered. The derivation of these will be examined in detail. After this, the states for which there is an angular variation of the wave function will be discussed more briefly, the results of the last chapter being used.

In this problem it is inappropriate to use cartesian coordinates, as may be seen if an expression for the potential energy is written down in those coordinates. It will be supposed that the nucleus is located at the origin and it will be regarded as stationary there (i.e. infinitely heavy). Polar coordinates will be used. These specify any point in terms of the distance from the origin, r, and two angular coordinates θ and ϕ which are defined in the manner described in the last chapter (Section III.6).

IV.2 Spherically Symmetrical Wave Functions of the Hydrogen Atom

For these functions $\dfrac{\partial \psi}{\partial \phi}$, $\dfrac{\partial^2 \psi}{\partial \phi^2}$, and $\dfrac{\partial \psi}{\partial \theta}$, $\dfrac{\partial^2 \psi}{\partial \theta^2}$, etc., are zero. Therefore it is only necessary to consider the transformation of the three-dimensional Schrödinger equation in cartesian coordinates (I.11) to one involving $\dfrac{\partial \psi}{\partial r}$ and $\dfrac{\partial^2 \psi}{\partial r^2}$. This is carried out in Appendix II. The result is

$$\frac{\partial^2 \psi}{\partial r^2} + \frac{2}{r} \cdot \frac{\partial \psi}{\partial r} + \frac{8\pi^2 m}{h^2}(E - V)\psi = 0, \qquad \text{(IV.1)}$$

where m is the mass of the electron. Let the charge on the nucleus be Ze (so that the treatment includes He^+, Li^{++}, etc.) and the charge on the electron be $-e$. Then

$$V = -\frac{Ze^2}{r}, \qquad (IV.2)$$

the zero of the energy scale being taken to be that of the nucleus and electron separated by an infinitely large distance. On this scale, E will be negative for the states in which the electron is bound to the nucleus. For convenience let

$$-\frac{8\pi^2 mE}{h^2} = \alpha^2 \qquad (IV.3)$$

and

$$\frac{8\pi^2 m}{h^2} \cdot Ze^2 = \beta. \qquad (IV.4)$$

So IV.1 may be written more briefly as

$$\frac{d^2\psi}{dr^2} + \frac{2}{r} \cdot \frac{d\psi}{dr} + \left(\frac{\beta}{r} - \alpha^2\right)\psi = 0. \qquad (IV.5)$$

Let us first examine the behaviour when r is very large so that the terms involving $\frac{1}{r}$ can be neglected. Then equation IV.5 becomes

$$\frac{d^2\psi}{dr^2} = \alpha^2\psi, \qquad (IV.6)$$

the solution of which is

$$\psi = e^{+\alpha r} \quad \text{or} \quad e^{-\alpha r}. \qquad (IV.7)$$

The normalisation constant is omitted from this partial solution; it can be included later. The first of the above solutions ($e^{+\alpha r}$) is unsatisfactory, as ψ would rise to infinity as r increased to infinity. The second ($e^{-\alpha r}$) is a satisfactory solution for it is finite for all values of r.

Returning to the original equation IV.5 let us test the possibility of finding a solution which is a product of this ($e^{-\alpha r}$) and another function, the second function being one that modifies $e^{-\alpha r}$ when r is small but allows the behaviour of the whole function to remain $e^{-\alpha r}$ as r approaches infinity. Let us, in particular, test the possibility of there being a solution of the form

$$\psi = e^{-\alpha r}.F(r), \qquad \text{(IV.8)}$$

where $F(r)$ is a polynomial in r. That is

$$F(r) = a_0 + a_1 r + a_2 r^2 + \ldots + a_s r^s + \ldots$$
$$= \Sigma \, a_s r^s. \qquad \text{(IV.9)}$$

In order to discover the precise form of $F(r)$ (now to be written as F), IV.8 is substituted into IV.5:

$$\left(\frac{d^2 F}{dr^2} e^{-\alpha r} - 2\alpha . e^{-\alpha r} . \frac{dF}{dr} + \alpha^2 . e^{-\alpha r} F\right)$$
$$+ \frac{2}{r}\left(e^{-\alpha r} . \frac{dF}{dr} - \alpha . e^{-\alpha r} F\right) + \left(\frac{\beta}{r} - \alpha^2\right) e^{-\alpha r} F = 0. \quad \text{(IV.10)}$$

This simplifies to

$$\frac{d^2 F}{dr^2} + \frac{dF}{dr}\left(\frac{2}{r} - 2\alpha\right) + F\left(\frac{\beta}{r} - \frac{2\alpha}{r}\right) = 0. \qquad \text{(IV.11)}$$

Substituting IV.9 gives

$$\Sigma \, a_{s+2}(s+2)(s+1)r^s$$
$$+ \left(\frac{2}{r} - 2\alpha\right)\Sigma \, a_{s+1}(s+1)r^s + \left(\frac{\beta}{r} - \frac{2\alpha}{r}\right)\Sigma \, a_s . r^s = 0. \quad \text{(IV.12)}$$

In this, the summations are for $s = 0, 1, 2 \ldots$ Gathering together the coefficients of r^{s-1} this is equivalent to

$$\Sigma \, \{a_{s+1}s(s+1) + 2(s+1)a_{s+1} - 2s.\alpha a_s$$
$$+ \beta . a_s - 2\alpha a_s\}r^{s-1} = 0, \qquad \text{(IV.13)}$$

where the summation is still for $s = 0, 1, 2, 3 \ldots$

Equation IV.13 is of the form

$$A_{-1}r^{-1} + A_0 + A_1 r + A_2 r^2 + \ldots = 0 \qquad \text{(IV.14)}$$

and is to be satisfied for *all* values of r. Since the L.H.S. must not go to infinity as r approaches zero, A_{-1} must be zero. Further, since the L.H.S. is to be zero at $r = 0$, A_0 must be zero. Let the L.H.S. be called the function A. If this is to remain zero as we move away from zero then $\frac{dA}{dr}, \frac{d^2 A}{dr^2}, \frac{d^3 A}{dr^3}$, etc., at $r = 0$ must all be zero and hence A_1, A_2, A_3, etc., must all be zero. Consequently IV.13 is only satisfied if, for all values of s $(0, 1, 2 \ldots)$,

D

$$(s + 1)(s + 2)a_{s+1} - \{2(s + 1)\alpha - \beta\}a_s = 0. \quad \text{(IV.15)}$$

That is
$$a_{s+1} = a_s \cdot \frac{2(s + 1)\alpha - \beta}{(s + 1)(s + 2)}. \quad \text{(IV.16)}$$

This equation serves to define the polynomial $F(r)$ so that IV.8 satisfies the Schrödinger equation. It is called a *recursion formula*. That is, if a_0 is chosen, a_1 can then be calculated in terms of a_0, and then a_2 in terms of a_1 and so on. Hence a satisfactory solution of the Schrödinger equation has been found. It takes the form IV.8, the polynomial $F(r)$ being defined by IV.9 and IV.16. The initial coefficient a_0 can then be fixed subsequently so as to normalise the wave function.

This solution must, however, be examined further to see whether it satisfies condition (i) of Chapter I, Section 3. It satisfies (ii) and (iii), being both single-valued and continuous. At small values of r it is clearly satisfactory. But, how does it behave at large values of r? In this region the terms involving r^s for which s is large will become increasingly important. For large values of s the recursion formula IV.16 becomes

$$a_{s+1} = a_s \cdot \frac{2\alpha}{s}. \quad \text{(IV.17)}$$

Now
$$e^{kx} = 1 + kx + \frac{k^2 x^2}{\lfloor 2} + \frac{k^3 x^3}{\lfloor 3} + \frac{k^4 x^4}{\lfloor 4} + \cdots$$

The recursion formula for this is

$$a_{s+1} = a_s \cdot \frac{k}{s + 1}. \quad \text{(IV.18)}$$

Comparing IV.18 with IV.17, remembering that, as s becomes increasingly large, the difference between s and $s + 1$ becomes insignificant, it is clear that $F(r)$ behaves like $e^{+2\alpha r}$. This means that ψ in IV.8 behaves like $e^{\alpha r}$. This is unsatisfactory (condition (i)) because ψ would approach infinity as r approached infinity.

There is a way out of this difficulty, which arises because of the behaviour of those terms in $F(r)$ which involve high powers of r. Consider the situation if $F(r)$ is not a polynomial with an unlimited number of terms, but contains only a limited number. In that case the above difficulty would not arise. However, can $F(r)$ be limited in this way and yet remain a satisfactory solution of the Schrödinger equation? The answer is: Yes. Consider the recursion formula IV.16. Suppose, for some value of s, that

$$2(s + 1)\alpha - \beta = 0. \qquad \text{(IV.19)}$$

Then a_{s+1} will be zero and the recursion formula will require that every further coefficient shall be zero. Therefore, if IV.19 is true for some value of s, terms involving high powers of r will be missing from $F(r)$, and the behaviour of ψ at large values of r will be controlled by $e^{-\alpha r}$, and it will therefore be satisfactory. Using the expressions for α and β (IV.3 and IV.4), IV.19 becomes

$$- 4(s + 1)^2 . \frac{8\pi^2 mE}{h^2} = \left(\frac{8\pi^2 mZe^2}{h^2} \right)^2, \qquad \text{(IV.20)}$$

from which

$$E = - \frac{2\pi^2 m . Z^2 e^4}{n^2 h^2}, \qquad \text{(IV.21)}$$

where $n = s + 1$ and can have the integral values 1, 2, 3, . . . Just as in the case of the particle in the box, the conditions required for satisfactory solutions provide a limitation on the form of the wave function, and, as a result, only certain values of the energy are possible. That is, the energy is quantised according to equation IV.21, which is identical with the expression obtained by Bohr for the energy levels of the hydrogen atom.

IV.3 Spherically Symmetric Wave Functions

Expressing equation IV.19 in terms of n we get*

$$\beta = 2n\alpha. \qquad \text{(IV.22)}$$

For the lowest level, $n = 1$ and $\beta = 2\alpha$. Then, from the recursion formula, for $s = 0$,

$$a_1 = a_0 . \frac{2\alpha - 2\alpha}{2} = 0 \qquad \text{(IV.23)}$$

and $a_2 = a_3 = a_4 = $ . . . 0 also. The wave function is therefore

$$\psi_1 = a_0 . e^{-\alpha r}. \qquad \text{(IV.24)}$$

---

* In this section it must be remembered that n fixes the term at which the function F will break off. Whatever the value of n, the recursion formula will be true for any value of s.

For the second level $n = 2$ and $\beta = 4\alpha$. The recursion formula with $s = 0$ gives

$$a_1 = a_0 \cdot \frac{2\alpha - 4\alpha}{2} = -\alpha . a_0, \tag{IV.25}$$

and with $s = 1$

$$a_2 = a_1 \cdot \frac{4\alpha - 4\alpha}{6} = 0. \tag{IV.26}$$

The wave function is therefore

$$\psi_2 = a_0(1 - \alpha r)e^{-\alpha r}. \tag{IV.27}$$

For the third level $n = 3$ and $\beta = 6\alpha$. The recursion formula with $s = 0$ gives

$$a_1 = a_0 \cdot \frac{2\alpha - 6\alpha}{2} = -2\alpha . a_0, \tag{IV.28}$$

with $s = 1$ gives

$$a_2 = a_1 \cdot \frac{4\alpha - 6\alpha}{6} = -\frac{\alpha}{3}a_1 = \frac{2\alpha^2}{3}a_0, \tag{IV.29}$$

and with $s = 2$ gives

$$a_3 = a_2 \cdot \frac{6\alpha - 6\alpha}{12} = 0. \tag{IV.30}$$

The wave function is therefore

$$\psi_3 = a_0\left(1 - 2\alpha r + \frac{2\alpha^2 r^2}{3}\right)e^{-\alpha r}. \tag{IV.31}$$

In these expressions (using IV.3 and IV.21)

$$\alpha^2 = \frac{8\pi^2 m}{h^2} \cdot \frac{2\pi^2 m . Z^2 e^4}{n^2 h^2}. \tag{IV.32}$$

Therefore

$$\alpha = \frac{4\pi^2 m . Z e^2}{n h^2}. \tag{IV.33}$$

That is, α is dependent on the quantum number, n. The value of $\frac{1}{\alpha}$, for $n = 1$ and $Z = 1$, is $\frac{h^2}{4\pi^2 m e^2}$. This is the quantity known as the Bohr radius ρ, being the value obtained by Bohr for the radius of orbit of the electron in the lowest state of the hydrogen atom.

Consequently the above wave functions may be written for the hydrogen atom as

$$\psi_1 = N_1 . e^{-\frac{r}{\rho}}, \tag{IV.34}$$

$$\psi_2 = N_2\left(1 - \frac{r}{2\rho}\right)e^{-\frac{r}{2\rho}}, \tag{IV.35}$$

$$\psi_3 = N_3\left(1 - \frac{2r}{3\rho} + \frac{2r^2}{27\rho^2}\right)e^{-\frac{r}{3\rho}}. \tag{IV.36}$$

The normalising constants, found by the same procedure as for the particle in the box, by integrating ψ^2 over the whole of space, and setting the integral equal to one, are

$$N_1 = \frac{1}{\sqrt{\pi}} \cdot \left(\frac{1}{\rho}\right)^{\frac{3}{2}}, \tag{IV.37}$$

$$N_2 = \frac{1}{2\sqrt{2\pi}} \cdot \left(\frac{1}{\rho}\right)^{\frac{3}{2}}, \tag{IV.38}$$

and

$$N_3 = \frac{1}{3\sqrt{3\pi}} \cdot \left(\frac{1}{\rho}\right)^{\frac{3}{2}}. \tag{IV.39}$$

The three wave functions ψ_1, ψ_2 and ψ_3 are shown graphically in Figure 6. There is the same behaviour as regards the number of

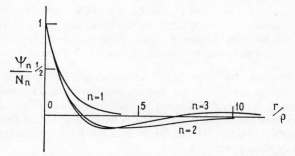

Fig. 6. Radial wave functions of the hydrogen atom for the states having spherically symmetrical functions and the principal quantum number, n, equal to 1, 2 and 3

nodes as was found for the particle in the box. ψ_1 has no nodal surfaces, ψ_2 has one spherical nodal surface, ψ_3 has two and so on. This corresponds to an increase in 'kinetic' energy (de Broglie) but, because the space is not rigidly limited, and the potential energy is not constant, the situation is more complex than with the particle in the box.

There are two ways in which the probability function may be presented. The simple square of the wave function measures the

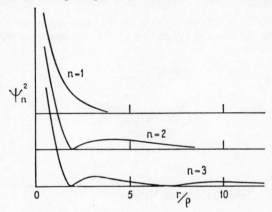

Fig. 7. Graphs of $\psi^2{}_n$ ($= P_u$, probability per unit volume) for the states of the hydrogen atom having spherically symmetric wave functions and the principal quantum number, n, equal to 1, 2 and 3

probability per unit volume (P_u). This is shown in Figure 7. This probability is greatest at the nucleus for all states. However, in many ways, a more illuminating probability is that of finding the electron between r and $r + dr$. The volume of the shell between these radii is $4\pi r^2 . dr$. Hence the probability $P_r . dr$ of finding the electron within that shell is

$$P_r . dr = 4\pi r^2 . \psi^2 . dr. \qquad \text{(IV.40)}$$

Graphs of $4\pi r^2 . \psi^2$ for the three states already considered are shown in Figure 8. This shows that the electron has a greater probability

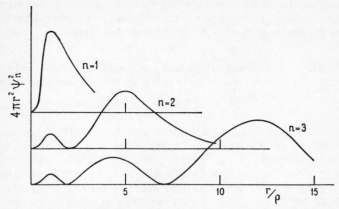

Fig. 8. Graphs of $4\pi r^2 \cdot \psi_n^2$ ($= P_r$, *probability at a radius) for the states of the hydrogen atom having spherically symmetric wave functions and the principal quantum number, n, equal to* 1, 2 *and* 3

of being in the region beyond the spherical node of largest radius, than between any of the other nodal surfaces. The two sets of curves in Figures 7 and 8 should be considered together because, despite the statement in the last sentence, the probability *per unit volume* is always greatest at the nucleus for states of the hydrogen atom having spherically symmetric wave functions.

IV.4 Complete Solutions for the Hydrogen Atom

In the last two sections the spherically symmetric solutions alone have been considered. In this section the solutions of the Schrödinger equation which involve all three polar coordinates will be presented. The equation is

$$\frac{\partial^2\psi}{\partial r^2} + \frac{2}{r}\cdot\frac{\partial\psi}{\partial r} + \frac{1}{r^2}\cdot\frac{\partial^2\psi}{\partial\theta^2} + \frac{\cos\theta}{r^2\sin\theta}\cdot\frac{\partial\psi}{\partial\theta}$$
$$+ \frac{1}{r^2\sin^2\theta}\cdot\frac{\partial^2\psi}{\partial\phi^2} + \frac{8\pi^2 m}{h^2}\left(E + \frac{Ze^2}{r}\right)\psi = 0. \quad \text{(IV.41)}$$

This may be derived from the Schrödinger equation in cartesian coordinates by a procedure similar to those given in Appendices I and II. The solution of IV.41 can be separated. That is

$$\psi(r, \theta, \phi) = R(r) . \Theta(\theta) . \Phi(\phi).$$ (IV.42)

If IV.42 is substituted in IV.41 and the angular part separated off in the usual way, it is found that the differential equation obtained is

$$\frac{1}{\Theta} . \frac{d^2\Theta}{d\theta^2} + \frac{\cos\theta}{\sin\theta} . \frac{1}{\Theta} . \frac{d\Theta}{d\theta} + \frac{1}{\sin^2\theta} . \frac{1}{\Phi} . \frac{d^2\Phi}{d\phi^2} + \beta = 0,$$ (IV.43)

where β is a constant. This is identical in form to III.37 (cf. also III.35 and III.39). Therefore the solutions to IV.43, giving the angular variation of the wave function, are identical with those listed in Section III.6 and described in III.7. Moreover, as in the last chapter, β is equal to $l(l + 1)$ where l is an integer (equation III.46). It follows therefore that the resulting equation for the radial function, R, is

$$\frac{d^2R}{dr^2} + \frac{2}{r} . \frac{dR}{dr} - \frac{l(l + 1)}{r^2}R + \frac{8\pi^2m}{h^2}\left(E + \frac{Ze^2}{r}\right)R = 0.$$ (IV.44)

For wave functions which are spherically symmetric $l = 0$. In this case the third term in IV.44 is zero, and IV.44 becomes identical with IV.1 which was the equation used for obtaining the spherically symmetric solutions. However, for the other solutions, equation IV.44 is dependent on the particular value of l, and therefore the radial wave functions are dependent on l. A similar situation was encountered in the last chapter for the particle on the surface of a sphere. There the solution for the function Θ was dependent on M and consequently on the form of the function Φ. However, the energy was independent of M, being dependent only on l, which was the quantum number appearing when the differential equation for Θ was solved. A similar situation occurs here. The radial function, R, obtained by solving IV.44, is dependent on the value of l, but the energy is dependent only on the quantum number, n, which is introduced when IV.44 is solved to give the R function. Moreover there is a further analogy. For the particle on the surface of a sphere l could not be less than M. In this case it is found that n must be greater than l. The situation is therefore that the energy for all states of the hydrogen atom is given by IV.21 in terms of a quantum number n. For a given value of n, l can assume the values 0, 1 ... $(n - 1)$. Further, as was found in the last chapter, M can assume any integral value from $-l$ to $+l$. Consequently the degeneracy of the successive energy levels is: $n = 1$, degeneracy $= 1$; $n = 2$, degeneracy $= 4$; $n = 3$, degeneracy $= 9$; $n = 4$, degeneracy $= 16$; and so on.

It is convenient to devise a system of symbols to describe the various states in a concise manner. For doing this values of l, the subsidiary quantum number, equal to 0, 1, 2 and 3 are represented by the letters s, p, d and f. The principal quantum number n is represented by the appropriate number. Therefore the state for which $n = 2$ and $l = 1$ is referred to as $2p$, and that for which $n = 4$ and $l = 2$ as $4d$. If it is necessary to specify the Φ part of the wave function (i.e. M), this is done by including a subscript. For example $2p_0$ represents $n = 2$, $l = 1$, $M = 0$; and $4d_{+1}$ represents $n = 4$, $l = 2$, $M = +1$. However, for the real forms of Φ subscripts involving cartesian coordinates are employed. For instance the three $2p$ functions are written as $2p_x$, $2p_y$ and $2p_z$ because $r \sin \theta . \cos \phi = x$, $r \sin \theta . \sin \phi = y$ and $r \cos \theta = z$. For the five $3d$ functions the following can be used: $3d_{3z^2-1}$ or, for brevity, $3d_{z^2}$, when $M = 0$; $3d_{xz}$ and $3d_{yz}$ for $|M| = 1$, the former representing $\sin \theta . \cos \theta \cos \phi$ and the latter $\sin \theta . \cos \theta \sin \phi$; and $3d_{xy}$ and $3d_{x^2-y^2}$ for $|M| = 2$, the former representing $\sin^2 \theta . \sin 2\phi$ and the latter $\sin^2 \theta . \cos 2\phi$.

IV.5 The Radial Wave Functions

The radial wave functions of the hydrogen atom $(Z = 1)$ are $e^{-\frac{r}{n\varrho}} . F(r)$. The functions $F(r)$ are listed in Table II. The normalisation constants have been omitted. The units used are those that were employed in Section IV.3, ρ being the Bohr radius $\left(\dfrac{h^2}{4\pi^2 me} \right)$.

Three of the radial functions for $l = 0$ were plotted in Figure 6. The first two functions for $l = 1$ are plotted in Figure 9. For these, $R = 0$ at the origin (this is true for all functions for which $l \neq 0$). For the successive radial functions in Figure 9, the number

TABLE II

n	$l = 0$	1	2	3
1	1	—	—	—
2	$1-\dfrac{1}{2}\cdot\dfrac{r}{\rho}$	$\dfrac{r}{\rho}$	—	—
3	$1-\dfrac{2}{3}\cdot\dfrac{r}{\rho}+\dfrac{2}{27}\cdot\dfrac{r^2}{\rho^2}$	$\dfrac{r}{\rho}\left(1-\dfrac{1}{6}\cdot\dfrac{r}{\rho}\right)$	$\dfrac{r^2}{\rho^2}$	—
4	$1-\dfrac{3}{4}\cdot\dfrac{r}{\rho}+\dfrac{1}{8}\cdot\dfrac{r^2}{\rho^2}-\dfrac{1}{192}\cdot\dfrac{r^3}{\rho^3}$	$\dfrac{r}{\rho}\left(1-\dfrac{1}{4}\cdot\dfrac{r}{\rho}+\dfrac{1}{80}\cdot\dfrac{r^2}{\rho^2}\right)$	$\dfrac{r^2}{\rho^2}\left(1-\dfrac{1}{12}\cdot\dfrac{r}{\rho}\right)$	$\dfrac{r^3}{\rho^3}$

of spherical nodal surfaces increases by one. It is apparent, from Table II, that the number of spherical nodal surfaces is equal to

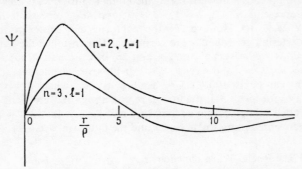

Fig. 9. Graphs of the radial wave functions of the hydrogen atom for states having (a) $n = 2$, $l = 1$; and (b) $n = 3$, $l = 1$

$(n - l - 1)$. Since the number of non-spherical nodal surfaces arising because of the form of the Θ and Φ functions is equal to l (cf. Section III.7), the total number of nodal surfaces is $(n - 1)$. For example, the $3s$ orbitals have two spherical nodal surfaces (cf. Figure 6), the $3p$ orbitals have one spherical and one planar one, the $3d$ have no spherical, but there are two non-spherical nodal surfaces. For $3d_{z^2}$ there are two conical nodal surfaces while, for the other four $3d$ orbitals, there are two planar ones. For the $3s$, $3p$ and $3d$ orbitals, all of which have two nodal surfaces, the energy is the same. This is, as it were, an accident arising from the unique form of the potential energy $\left(V = -\dfrac{Ze^2}{r} \right)$.

For other forms of V which are spherically symmetric (i.e. functions of r only) the solutions of the Θ and Φ functions will be the same as for the hydrogen atom. This must be so, because the term involving V in IV.41 is removed when the angular function is being considered (equation IV.43), and only reappears when the radial function R is being determined (equation IV.44). It is because of this that the angular functions Θ and Φ, and the angular momenta associated with them, are so important.

The outermost electrons of atoms other than hydrogen may be regarded as moving in a field due to the nucleus and an inner core of electrons which is spherically symmetric. The result of this is that V is a function of r only, but it is more complicated than $-\dfrac{Ze^2}{r}$.

Consequently the effect of the spherical nodal surfaces becomes different from that of the non-spherical ones, and the energies associated with the different orbitals of the same n are no longer the same. In fact, the effect is that the energy of the ns orbital is less than that of the np, which is less than that of the nd and so on. The order of energies for the levels having the same l is of course still the order of n as it was for the hydrogen atom.

As regards the nodal surfaces for atoms other than hydrogen, the non-spherical ones are identical with those for the hydrogen atom (cf. earlier). The number of spherical nodal surfaces is the same as for the hydrogen atom, but the spacing is somewhat different because the form of the radial function is different.

When studying the spherically symmetrical solutions in Section IV.3, graphs were drawn of the wave functions (Figure 6), the probabilities per unit volume, P_u (Figure 7), and the probability for a particular radius, P_r (Figure 8). The $2p$ and $3p$ wave functions have been drawn in Figure 9. It is easy to see from these the form that

P_u would take. As regards P_r, the situation would be the same as Figure 8; namely that the probability of finding the particle beyond the largest spherical nodal surface is greater than that of finding it between any of the others.

IV.6 Conclusion

In this chapter a complete derivation was given for the spherically symmetrical wave functions of the hydrogen atom, an expression being obtained for the energies. The angular functions were the same as those obtained in the last chapter; the radial wave functions for the non-spherical solutions were then listed. Because the problem is three-dimensional there are three quantum numbers. These are n, which specifies the energy, l, which specifies the total angular momentum, and M, which specifies the angular momentum about a selected axis. For a given value of n, l is restricted to the integers which are less than n; the values allowed for M are also limited. For atoms other than hydrogen, the one-electron angular wave functions will be the same and consequently the quantisation of angular momentum will remain unaltered. The radial functions will, however, be different. Nevertheless the wave functions can still be specified in terms of the number, and form, of the nodal surfaces so that the descriptions $1s$, $2p$, $3d$, etc., retain their usefulness for all atomic systems.

CHAPTER V

Approximate Methods

V.1 Introduction

In the preceding chapter the systems considered have been those for which the Schrödinger equation can be solved exactly, the true wave functions, energies and other properties being obtained. However, this is not the situation that exists for most problems that are of chemical interest; for these, approximate methods have to be employed. The two most important are known as the *perturbation method* and the *variation method*. This chapter describes the procedures involved in these two methods and illustrates them by a simple example. In the two following chapters, the various treatments that have been applied to the ground states of the helium atom and the hydrogen molecule will be described.

In the examples treated in the last three chapters, the problem was the determination of the functions which satisfied a differential equation containing an adjustable constant (E); the functions being subject to certain restrictions. This is, in effect, always the problem but, in all but the simplest examples, it cannot be solved. In such cases a trial wave function is employed, and the *mean energy* corresponding to this function is calculated. This is taken to be the energy of the system. Unfortunately, in many cases of chemical interest, it is extremely difficult to judge what the true wave function will be like. Further, the labour involved in estimating the mean energy is often so great that it is necessary to limit, in some way, the trial function that is used. As a result of these difficulties the choosing of the trial wave functions has become, in many ways, more of an *art* than a *science*. It is the aim of much that is contained in the following chapters to illustrate and examine the approximations that have been used, and the results that have been obtained from them, for a variety of atomic and molecular systems.

V.2 Perturbation Method

This method is suitable for problems which differ in some way, which is preferably small, from ones for which an exact solution is known. For example, it can be applied very successfully to the action of a weak electric field on the hydrogen atom. The wave functions and energies are known exactly for all states of the hydrogen atom in the absence of the field. The weak electric field constitutes what is called a *perturbation* to the system. In such a situation the perturbation method is an effective one.

The perturbation method will be described in general terms for a system consisting of one particle in one dimension. This is adequate to show the nature of the method. Let the potential energy for the unperturbed system for which exact solutions are available be V. Let the potential energy arising from the perturbation be V'. This, like V, will be a function of the coordinate x. Let the wave functions, which are solutions of the Schrödinger equation for the unperturbed system (i.e. for V alone), be $\psi_1, \psi_2, \psi_3, \ldots \psi_n$, and the corresponding energies $E_1, E_2, E_3 \ldots E_n$. For the present let us suppose that the functions are normalised and real, and the states nondegenerate. It follows by rearranging the Schrödinger equation that the energies, E_n, are given by:

$$E_n = \frac{1}{\psi_n}\left\{-\frac{h^2}{8\pi^2 m}\cdot\frac{d^2\psi_n}{dx^2} + V\cdot\psi_n\right\}. \qquad (V.1)$$

It will be supposed that the effect of the perturbation on the wave function, and consequently the probability function, is so small that it can be ignored. This assumption that ψ_n and ψ_n^2 are unaffected is the essential feature of the, so-called, first order perturbation method, and it is because of this that it is most successful when the perturbation is small. By analogy with V.1 we may write:

$$\frac{1}{\psi_n}\left\{-\frac{h^2}{8\pi^2 m}\cdot\frac{d^2\psi_n}{dx^2} + (V + V')\psi_n\right\}. \qquad (V.2)$$

This gives a quantity having the dimensions of energy but its value will vary with x, the position of the particle.

Because ψ_n is the solution of the unperturbed problem the application of the operator in V.1 leads to a constant E_n which is the energy. Because ψ_n is not the true solution for the perturbed problem, formula V.2 will not lead to a constant. The total 'energy' calculated according to V.2 varies with position. In the perturbation method, the energy for each position of the particle is multiplied by the probability of that configuration and the 'weighted' energy is integrated over the whole of space. This is equivalent to determining the *mean* of the fluctuating energy that is obtained from V.2, the energy of each configuration being weighted according to the probability of that configuration. This procedure will now be set out in mathematical terms.

The energy of each configuration as obtained by V.2 is multiplied by the probability $\psi_n{}^2$ giving:

$$\frac{\psi_n{}^2}{\psi_n}\left\{-\frac{h^2}{8\pi^2 m}\cdot\frac{d^2\psi_n}{dx^2}+(V+V')\psi_n\right\}$$
$$=\psi_n\left\{-\frac{h^2}{8\pi^2 m}\cdot\frac{d^2\psi_n}{dx^2}+(V+V')\psi_n\right\}. \quad \text{(V.3)}$$

By making use of V.1, namely that the functions ψ_n are the solutions for the unperturbed system, this can be simplified to

$$\psi_n\{E_n\psi_n + V'\psi_n\}. \quad \text{(V.4)}$$

Integration gives:

$$\int_{-\infty}^{+\infty}\psi_n.E_n.\psi_n.dx + \int_{-\infty}^{+\infty}\psi_n.V'.\psi_n.dx. \quad \text{(V.5)}$$

Because E_n is a constant V.5 can be written as

$$E_n\int_{-\infty}^{+\infty}\psi_n{}^2.dx + \int_{-\infty}^{+\infty}V'.\psi_n{}^2.dx. \quad \text{(V.6)}$$

This gives, because ψ_n is normalised,

$$\bar{E} = E_n + \int_{-\infty}^{+\infty}V'.\psi_n{}^2.dx. \quad \text{(V.7)}$$

The mean energy is different from the unperturbed value by E' which is given by:

$$E' = \int_{-\infty}^{+\infty}V'.\psi_n{}^2.dx. \quad \text{(V.8)}$$

The perturbation energy, E', is therefore equal to the perturbation for each configuration, V', multiplied by the probability of that configuration, ψ_n^2, the product being integrated over the whole of the space. This is equivalent to taking a weighted mean.

If ψ_n is imaginary, then ψ_n^2 must be replaced by $\psi_n . \psi_n^*$. If ψ_n is not normalised, let $N . \psi_n$ be the normalised function. Then

$$\int_{-\infty}^{+\infty} (N.\psi_n)^2 \, dx = 1 \qquad (V.9)$$

and, because N is a constant,

$$N^2 = \frac{1}{\displaystyle\int_{-\infty}^{+\infty} \psi_n^2 . dx} . \qquad (V.10)$$

In this event V.6 must be modified as follows:

$$\begin{aligned}
E' &= \int_{-\infty}^{+\infty} V'(N.\psi_n)^2 . dx \\
&= N^2 \int_{-\infty}^{+\infty} V'.\psi_n^2 . dx \\
&= \frac{\displaystyle\int_{-\infty}^{+\infty} V'.\psi_n^2 . dx}{\displaystyle\int_{-\infty}^{+\infty} \psi_n^2 . dx} \qquad (V.11)
\end{aligned}$$

If ψ_n is both imaginary and not normalised,

$$E' = \frac{\displaystyle\int_{-\infty}^{+\infty} V'.\psi_n.\psi_n^* . dx}{\displaystyle\int_{-\infty}^{+\infty} \psi_n.\psi_n^* . dx} \qquad (V.12)$$

This is the most general form of the expression for E'. It involves only a simple development of V.8.

The weakness of this perturbation method lies in the assumption that the perturbation does not modify the wave function and the probability function. In many cases, particularly when the perturbation is not small, this assumption is most unsatisfactory and, because of its obvious incorrectness, it might have been expected that the perturbation method would be an unsuccessful one. This is not so and in certain cases it is unexpectedly successful. For example, with the ground state of the helium atom, the perturbation being the inter-electron repulsion, E' is found to be only 14% greater than the difference between the true energy and the unperturbed energy of the system. This is particularly surprising because, in this instance, the perturbation cannot be regarded as a small one. It would seem therefore that, in this, and in other cases also, either the wave function shows a stability to distortion so that the wave function for the perturbed system is not very different from that for the un-perturbed one, or the energy is not very susceptible to quite con-siderable changes in the wave function. However, there is one major difficulty of this method. Unless an experimental result is available it is impossible to know how different the calculated energy is from the true one; that is, how good an approximation has been achieved.

V.3 The Variation Method

This method is of importance for determining the energy of the lowest state of the system. In special cases it can be applied to other states but, at first, only the lowest state of all will be con-sidered. The strength of the method is derived from the *Variation Theorem*. As in the last section, the theorem and method will be illustrated in terms of a single particle system in one dimension. The extension to more particles in more dimensions follows naturally.

Take a trial function χ which is normalised. Then, for any position of the particle, the 'energy' is given by

$$E = \frac{1}{\chi}\left\{ - \frac{h^2}{8\pi^2 m}\cdot\frac{d^2\chi}{dx^2} + V.\chi \right\}, \qquad \text{(V.13)}$$

where V is the potential energy. The 'mean energy' for the various configurations, weighted according to the probability of the con-figurations, is then given, as in the last section, by

$$\bar{E} = \int_{-\infty}^{+\infty} \chi\left\{ - \frac{h^2}{8\pi^2 m}\cdot\frac{d^2\chi}{dx^2} + V\chi \right\}.dx. \qquad \text{(V.14)}$$

The variation theorem states that $\bar{E}$ is *always* greater than the true energy of the lowest state of the system. Unfortunately the theorem does not provide any means of telling how much greater $\bar{E}$ is than

E

the true energy. However, in suitable cases, this method can be used to obtain extremely good values for the energy (e.g. the helium atom and the hydrogen molecule). Often the following procedure is used to take the maximum advantage of the theorem. The function χ is defined so that it contains one or more adjustable constants, the values of which are left undetermined initially. Then the value of $\bar{E}$ is determined by equation V.14. This $\bar{E}$ is a function of the, as yet, undetermined constants. These constants are then chosen so that $\bar{E}$ is minimised. Because $\bar{E}$ must be greater than the true energy, this ensures that $\bar{E}$ is as close to the true energy as is possible within the limitation of the type of function selected. The more flexible the original trial function χ, and the more undetermined constants it contains, the closer will the minimised $\bar{E}$ be to the true energy. With this method, therefore, the choice of the initial function is of the greatest importance. A great deal depends on the skill and in-genuity with which the initial choice of χ is made. It would appear, from what has been said, that any desired accuracy could be achieved by this method. However, the more flexible is the trial function, the more terms it contains, and the more labour and time is involved in evaluating the integrals resulting from substituting it into V.14. Moreover certain integrals prove intractable, so that sometimes it is not possible to give to the trial function the form one would wish. In practice a balance must be struck between the desire for greater accuracy on the one hand, and the time and labour involved on the other. With the advent of high-speed com-puters it is now possible, in many cases, to reduce the time required for the evaluation of V.14, so that there is considerable hope that the variation method will become of even greater value.

As in the last section, in the event of the trial function not being normalised, V.14 becomes:

$$\bar{E} = \frac{\int_{-\infty}^{+\infty} \chi \left\{ -\frac{h^2}{8\pi^2 m} \cdot \frac{d^2\chi}{dx^2} + V\chi \right\} . dx}{\int_{-\infty}^{+\infty} \chi . \chi . dx}. \tag{V.15}$$

If χ involves imaginary terms then the first χ in both integrals in V.15 must be replaced by χ^*.

V.4 An Example of the Perturbation and Variation Methods

Because of the importance of these two methods to the chemist a simple example will be worked out in detail. The example will be 'a particle in a ring'. The perturbation will consist of reducing the potential energy to $-\dfrac{1}{2}\cdot\dfrac{h^2}{8\pi^2 I}$ between $\phi = -\dfrac{\pi}{6}$ and $\phi = +\dfrac{\pi}{6}$, the potential energy remaining zero over the rest of the circle. That is the potential energy for the perturbed problem is a stepped function. It is zero between $\dfrac{\pi}{6}$ and $\dfrac{11\pi}{6}$, and $-\dfrac{1}{2}\cdot\dfrac{h^2}{8\pi^2 I}$ between $-\dfrac{\pi}{6}$ and $\dfrac{\pi}{6}$ $\left(-\dfrac{\pi}{6}\text{ represents the same point on the circle as }\dfrac{11\pi}{6}\right)$. The perturbation is given as a simple multiple of $\dfrac{h^2}{8\pi^2 I}$ because the energies of the system were obtained as simple multiples of $\dfrac{h^2}{8\pi^2 I}$ (cf. Section III.2).

The unperturbed energy of the lowest state is zero (equation III.10). The true energy of the lowest state of the new system can, in this case, be determined by exact methods and is $-0.1014\dfrac{h^2}{8\pi^2 I}$.

The unperturbed wave function is

$$\psi_0 = \frac{1}{\sqrt{2\pi}}. \tag{V.16}$$

This is normalised. To obtain a value for the energy by the perturbation method the perturbation, V', is multiplied by ψ_0^2 and the result integrated over the whole of the space. Since the potential energy is only reduced between $-\dfrac{\pi}{6}$ and $+\dfrac{\pi}{6}$ this is achieved by integrating over that range:

$$\int_{-\frac{\pi}{6}}^{+\frac{\pi}{6}} -\frac{1}{2}\cdot\frac{h^2}{8\pi^2 I}\cdot\frac{1}{2\pi}\cdot d\phi = -\frac{1}{2}\cdot\frac{h^2}{8\pi^2 I}\cdot\frac{1}{2\pi}\cdot\frac{\pi}{3}$$

$$= \frac{1}{12}\cdot\frac{h^2}{8\pi^2 I} = -0.0833\frac{h^2}{8\pi^2 I}. \tag{V.17}$$

The energy lowering calculated by perturbation theory is therefore about 82% of the actual lowering.

The Variation Method will now be applied to this system. As stated above, the success achieved by this method is dependent on the cleverness with which the trial function is chosen. The choice of the trial function, which is to be used, will therefore be discussed first. The unperturbed function is constant all round the ring. The effect of adding the potential well between $\phi = -\frac{\pi}{6}$ and $+\frac{\pi}{6}$ must be to increase the probability of the particle being in that region at the expense of it being elsewhere. Therefore the unperturbed function must be modified so as to increase its value in the neighbourhood of $\phi = 0$, and to decrease its value in other parts. This can be done by combining the unperturbed function with the function $\cos \phi$ in the following way:

$$\chi = \frac{1}{\sqrt{2\pi}} + \frac{k}{\sqrt{\pi}} \cos \phi. \qquad (V.18)$$

The second term serves to increase the probability near $\phi = 0$ (between $-90°$ and $+90°$), and to decrease it in the neighbourhood of $180°$ (between $90°$ and $270°$). The constant k, measuring the extent of admixture, will be left undetermined and will ultimately be fixed so as to minimise the derived energy.

Now $\frac{1}{\sqrt{2\pi}}$ and $\frac{1}{\sqrt{\pi}} \cos \phi$ are normalised orthogonal functions for the unperturbed problem. Therefore

$$\int_0^{2\pi} \chi^2 . d\phi = 1 + k^2. \qquad (V.19)$$

The numerator of equation V.15 which is required to obtain $\bar{E}$ is

$$\int_0^{2\pi} \left(\frac{1}{\sqrt{2\pi}} + \frac{k}{\sqrt{\pi}} \cos \phi \right) \left[- \frac{h^2}{8\pi^2 I} . \frac{d^2}{d\phi^2} \left(\frac{1}{\sqrt{2\pi}} + \frac{k}{\sqrt{\pi}} \cos \phi \right) \right] d\phi$$

$$+ \int_{-\frac{\pi}{6}}^{+\frac{\pi}{6}} \left(- \frac{1}{2} . \frac{h^2}{8\pi^2 I} \right) \left(\frac{1}{\sqrt{2\pi}} + \frac{k}{\sqrt{\pi}} \cos \phi \right)^2 d\phi$$

$$= \frac{h^2}{8\pi^2 I}\left\{ \int_0^{2\pi} \left(\frac{1}{\sqrt{2\pi}} + \frac{k}{\sqrt{\pi}}\cos\phi \right)\left(-\frac{k}{\sqrt{\pi}}\cos\phi \right) d\phi \right.$$

$$\left. -\frac{1}{2}\int_{-\frac{\pi}{6}}^{+\frac{\pi}{6}} \left(\frac{1}{2\pi} + \frac{\sqrt{2}k}{\pi}\cos\phi + \frac{k^2}{\pi}\cos^2\phi \right) d\phi \right\}$$

$$= \frac{h^2}{8\pi^2 I}\left\{ k^2 - \frac{1}{2}\left(\frac{1}{6} + \frac{\sqrt{2}k}{\pi} + \frac{k^2}{6} + \frac{\sqrt{3}k^2}{4\pi} \right) \right\}. \quad \text{(V.20)}$$

Dividing V.19 by V.18 we obtain, using V.15,

$$\bar{E} = \frac{h^2}{8\pi^2 I}\left\{ -\frac{1}{12} - \frac{\dfrac{k}{\sqrt{2\pi}} - \left(1 - \dfrac{\sqrt{3}}{8\pi}\right)k^2}{1 + k^2} \right\}. \quad \text{(V.21)}$$

By evaluating $\dfrac{d\bar{E}}{dk}$ and setting it equal to zero it is found that $\bar{E}$ is minimised for $k = 0\cdot119$. When this value of k is substituted into V.21

$$\bar{E} = -0\cdot0967\frac{h^2}{8\pi^2 I}. \quad \text{(V.22)}$$

Therefore, by using this variation treatment, the reduction in energy caused by the perturbation has been calculated to be about 95% of its true value. This is very satisfactory. However, the labour involved in obtaining V.22 is very much greater than that involved in obtaining V.17 by the perturbation method. Moreover if an extra term, involving say cos 2ϕ, had been included in V.18 with a second adjustable parameter in order to improve the wave function and energy still further, the time and labour would have been very much greater than that involved in using V.18. The scale of time and labour involved in handling the present simple problem is, of course, very much less than that when molecular problems are being considered. In such problems, which are of practical interest to the chemist, the limitation of what can be dealt with in a reasonable time is a serious one.

The example has also illustrated that the application of both the perturbation and variation methods involves the evaluation of integrals. Consequently, in dealing with chemical problems, variation functions must be chosen which lead to integrals that can be evaluated. This also limits the choice that can be made for χ.

Returning to the solution of the variation function it was found that k in V.18 must be 0·119 to minimise $\bar{E}$. This seems surprisingly large considering that the use of the first term of V.18 (i.e. $k = 0$) gave the energy lowering as 86% of the true value. The change of k from 0 to 0·119 only reduced the error from the true energy by two-thirds of that error. This illustrates what is often found, namely that the energy is not very sensitive to what appear to be quite considerable changes in the wave function.

V.5 Application of Variation Method to Other States

The variation method is primarily important for ground states. However, it can be used, to a limited extent, for other states. Suppose the system under consideration is spherically symmetrical, e.g. the hydrogen atom. The wave function of the lowest state must be spherically symmetrical because the wave function must have no nodes. As a consequence the separate terms in any trial function (cf. equation V.18) would have to be spherically symmetric. However, certain wave functions for the hydrogen atom have planar nodal surfaces. For example, the $2p_x$ function has the yz plane as a planar nodal surface. In this case, the trial function for an atomic system, for which V was more complicated than just $-\dfrac{Ze^2}{r}$, would have to be made up of terms involving functions all of which had this same nodal plane. There could be no contributing spherically symmetric functions. Therefore the problem is entirely separate from the 'spherical one'. This means that, for an atomic system, the variation method could be applied to obtaining the energy of the lowest s state, the lowest p state, the lowest d state, etc. A similar situation exists in other problems. The variation method can be used to determine the energies of the lowest states corresponding to each symmetry type the wave function can have.

V.6 The Symbol H

Because of the length of such formulae as V.3, V.13, and V.15 it is profitable to introduce a new symbol which will lead to their abbreviation. Moreover for several particles in three dimensions the length and complexity of formulae such as V.15 would become prohibitive.

The Schrödinger equation for a single particle may be written

$$\frac{1}{\psi}\left\{-\frac{h^2}{8\pi m^2}\cdot\nabla^2\psi + V\psi\right\} = E. \tag{V.23}$$

The operator which gives the energy of the system is therefore

$$-\frac{h^2}{8\pi^2 m}\cdot\nabla^2 + V. \tag{V.24}$$

For brevity, this operator is represented by H, and called the *Hamiltonian operator* because of its relation to an expression introduced into classical mechanics by Hamilton. Therefore equation V.23 may be written as

$$\frac{1}{\psi}\cdot H\psi = E \quad \text{or} \quad H\psi = E\psi. \tag{V.25}$$

This is an abbreviated statement of the Schrödinger equation. The symbol H can be used for any number of particles because it is, in general, equivalent to

$$-\frac{h^2}{8\pi^2 m_1}\cdot\nabla_1{}^2 - \frac{h^2}{8\pi^2 m_2}\nabla_2{}^2 - \ \ldots\ + V, \tag{V.26}$$

where

$$\nabla_n{}^2 = \frac{\partial^2}{\partial x_n{}^2} + \frac{\partial^2}{\partial y_n{}^2} + \frac{\partial^2}{\partial z_n{}^2}, \tag{V.27}$$

x_n, y_n and z_n being the coordinates of the nth particle of mass m_n. The potential energy V is, in general, a function of the coordinates of all the particles.

By using this symbol H, the fundamental formula of the variation method V.15 may be written as

$$\bar{E} = \frac{\displaystyle\int \chi^* H\chi \, d\tau}{\displaystyle\int \chi^*\chi \, d\tau}. \tag{V.28}$$

This summarises the procedure, however complex the system, and whatever the trial function, χ. The symbol $d\tau$ represents a volume element. For one particle in one dimension it is dx, for one particle in three dimensions $dx\ dy\ dz$ and for n particles in three dimensions it is $dx_1\ dy_1\ dz_1\ dx_2 \ldots dy_n\ dz_n$. The integration must, of course, be carried out over as many variables as are involved in the problem.

V.7 Conclusion

In this chapter the two important procedures for obtaining approximate solutions have been described. They make use of functions which are not true solutions of the Schrödinger equation. Because of this, the term E in the equation is not constant but is a function of the coordinates. Both methods determine a weighted mean of this quantity, and regard this mean energy as the calculated energy of the system. The variation method is the more powerful of the two methods. Its merit for ground states resides in the Variation Theorem which states that this mean energy is greater than the true one. By systematising the choice of the trial function, the energy calculated by the variation method can be brought very close to the true energy in favourable cases.

The perturbation method described in this chapter is the most simple one. There are other perturbation methods which are more lengthy than the one described here. Since most molecules of chemical interest are complicated and contain many electrons it is usually only possible to apply the more simple procedures. The use of more complicated ones often requires an amount of labour which would probably render their application impossible. Alternatively the greater accuracy, which might be achieved, would not justify the additional time that would be required.

It is important to realise that, when problems of chemical interest are treated by these approximate methods, drastic simplifications have to be made. It is important to be able to assess as far as possible the errors that may result from these simplifications. This is usually extremely difficult, and hence it is, as yet, almost impossible in most cases to judge the reliability of predictions of wave mechanical calculations except by comparison with experiment.

CHAPTER VI

The Helium Atom

VI.1 Introduction

In this chapter the perturbation and variation methods will be applied to the ground state of the helium atom. As with the hydrogen atom, the nucleus will be assumed to be at the origin and the behaviour of the two electrons only will be examined. This is, therefore, the first *two-particle* system that has been considered in this book. Moreover it is one for which the potential energy depends on the distance between the two particles. It is this repulsion between the two particles which prevents the exact solution of the problem, and necessitates the employment of the approximate methods described in the last chapter. For no problem involving more than one electron has it been possible to solve the Schrödinger equation exactly. However, in simple two-electron systems, such as the helium atom and the hydrogen molecule, such flexible trial functions can be used with the variation method that almost any desired accuracy can be obtained.

Later in this chapter, some more fundamental properties of systems containing two or more electrons will be considered. This will involve the introduction of a further postulate, the Pauli Principle. It is also necessary at this stage to take account of the 'spin' of the electron.

So far, the function that is the exact or approximate solution of the Schrödinger equation for a single particle has been referred to as the wave function. Because we are about to consider atomic and molecular systems it is convenient to introduce a new term. Single-particle wave functions which are the exact or approximate solutions of the Schrödinger equation for atomic and molecular systems will be referred to as *orbitals*. The word was chosen because these *orbitals* replaced the older Bohr–Sommerfeld orbits, which were executed by each electron.

VI.2 A Perturbation Treatment of the Ground State of the Helium Atom

The helium singly charged ion, He^+, resembles a hydrogen atom, but the charge on the nucleus is twice as great. As a result, the energies of the various states are four times as big (equation IV.21). The scale of the wave functions is also affected. The change is summarised in equation IV.33. In effect, r is scaled down by a factor of 2. Therefore the wave function for the ground state is

$$\psi_1 = N_1 . e^{-\frac{2r}{\rho}}. \tag{VI.1}$$

For the perturbation treatment, the unperturbed system will be taken to be a hypothetical helium atom in which the electrons do not repel one another. For the ground state both electrons will be in the lowest state ($1s$). Since they exert no force on one another they behave independently. Therefore the energy is twice as great as that of the one electron in He^+. The energy is therefore $2(-4E_H) = -8E_H$, where $-E_H$ is the energy of a hydrogen atom in its lowest state.* The wave function for this unperturbed state is

$$\left(N_1 . e^{-\frac{2r_1}{\rho}}\right)\left(N_1 . e^{-\frac{2r_2}{\rho}}\right), \tag{VI.2}$$

where r_1 and r_2 are the distances of the two electrons, 1 and 2, from the nucleus.

The real helium atom differs from the above hypothetical one by the repulsion potential between the two electrons. This repulsion potential will therefore be treated as the perturbation (V'):

$$V' = +\frac{e^2}{r_{12}}, \tag{VI.3}$$

where r_{12} is the distance between the two electrons, 1 and 2. Therefore, by analogy with V.8, the perturbation energy is

$$E' = \int \int \frac{e^2}{r_{12}} . \left(N_1 . e^{-\frac{2r_1}{\rho}}\right)^2 \left(N_1 . e^{-\frac{2r_2}{\rho}}\right)^2 d\tau_1 . d\tau_2. \tag{VI.4}$$

---

* This would only be exactly true if both the hydrogen and helium nuclei were infinitely heavy.

Where $d\tau_1$ and $d\tau_2$ are the volume elements for the electrons 1 and 2 (cf. section V.6).* Alternatively, if the unperturbed function has been used in the form

$$\psi_0 = e^{-\frac{2r_1}{\rho}} . e^{-\frac{2r_2}{\rho}}, \qquad (VI.5)$$

which is not normalised, the expression for the perturbation energy is analogous to V.11, namely

$$E' = \frac{\displaystyle\iint \frac{e^2}{r_{12}} \left(e^{-\frac{2r_1}{\rho}} . e^{-\frac{2r_2}{\rho}}\right)^2 d\tau_1 \, d\tau_2}{\displaystyle\iint \left(e^{-\frac{2r_1}{\rho}} . e^{-\frac{2r_2}{\rho}}\right)^2 d\tau_1 \, d\tau_2}. \qquad (VI.6)$$

The evaluation of the integrals in VI.6, which is not difficult, leads to

$$E' = \tfrac{5}{2}E_H. \qquad (VI.7)$$

For any system that is like a helium atom (e.g. H^-, Li^+, Be^{++}, etc.) with a nuclear charge of Z the expression for E' is

$$E' = \tfrac{5}{4}ZE_H. \qquad (VI.8)$$

Therefore, a first order perturbation calculation of the energy of a helium atom gives $(-8E_H + \tfrac{5}{2}E_H)$, which is $-5\tfrac{1}{2}E_H$. The experimental value is about $-5\cdot8E_H$. The calculated electronic energy is about 95% of the true value. On the other hand, because the calculated and experimental energy of He^+ is $-4E_H$, the calculated ionisation potential is $1\cdot5E_H$, and the experimental $1\cdot8E_H$. The error in the calculation of this quantity is about 17%, whereas that for the total energy was only 5%. This type of difficulty is very common. It is often fairly easy to obtain quite good values for the total electronic energy of a system. The experimental quantities of interest are, however, the differences, often small, between the total electronic energies of two systems. As a consequence, small errors in total electronic energies can be very serious, when it is desired to make estimates of quantities that are observed experimentally. This is

---

* As stated in the last chapter the volume element $d\tau_1$ will be given, in cartesian coordinates, by $dx_1 \, dy_1 \, dz_1$. In polar coordinates, which are more appropriate here, $d\tau_1 = r_1^2 . \sin\theta_1 \, d\theta_1 \, d\phi_1 \, dr_1$ and similarly for $d\tau_2$. The integration is from 0 to π for θ, 0 to 2π for ϕ, and 0 to ∞ for r.

particularly true of chemically interesting quantities (e.g. dissociation energies) which are usually very small compared with the total electronic energies.

VI.3 A Variation Treatment of the Ground State of the Helium Atom

As always the first problem is how to choose the trial function. The unperturbed function used in the last section was a simple $1s$ wave function for a nuclear charge of 2. Inter-electron repulsion will result in an expansion of the *electron cloud*. Each electron will behave, approximately, because of the presence of the other electron, as if the nuclear charge is rather less than 2. In other words, the other electron *screens* some of the nuclear charge. This suggests that a possible trial function would be to replace $e^{-2\frac{r}{\rho}}$ by

$$\chi = e^{-Z'\frac{r}{\rho}} \qquad (VI.9)$$

where Z' is less than 2. As outlined in the last chapter, Z' can be left undetermined and $\bar{E}$ obtained as a function of Z'. The parameter Z' is then chosen to minimise $\bar{E}$. The expression for $\bar{E}$ is

$$\bar{E} = \frac{\iint e^{-Z'\frac{r_1}{\rho}} . e^{-Z'\frac{r_2}{\rho}} . H\left(e^{-Z'\frac{r_1}{\rho}} . e^{-Z'\frac{r_2}{\rho}}\right) d\tau_1 \, d\tau_2}{\iint \left(e^{-Z'\frac{r_1}{\rho}} . e^{-Z'\frac{r_2}{\rho}}\right)^2 d\tau_1 \, d\tau_2}, \qquad (VI.10)$$

where

$$H = -\frac{h^2}{8\pi^2 m}(\nabla_1{}^2 + \nabla_2{}^2) - \frac{2e^2}{r_1} - \frac{2e^2}{r_2} + \frac{e^2}{r_{12}}. \qquad (VI.11)$$

In polar coordinates:

$$\nabla^2 = \frac{\delta^2}{\delta r^2} + \frac{2}{r} . \frac{\delta}{\delta r} + \frac{1}{r^2} . \frac{\delta^2}{\delta \theta^2} + \frac{1}{r^2} . \frac{\cos\theta}{\sin\theta} . \frac{\delta}{\delta\theta} + \frac{1}{r^2 \sin^2\theta} . \frac{\delta^2}{\delta\phi^2}. \qquad (VI.12)$$

This replaces the expression in cartesian coordinates given in Section I.4. The solution of VI.10 leads to an expression for the energy which is minimised when Z' is put equal to $\frac{27}{16}$. The energy $\bar{E}$ is calculated to be $-5\cdot7E_H$ so that the error in the total energy has now been reduced to about $1\cdot7\%$, and that in the calculated ionisation potential to about 5%. The wave function which minimises the energy corresponds to an effective nuclear charge which is $\frac{5}{16}$ less than the true one. The *other* electron exerts a *screening effect* of $-\frac{5}{16}$. For any helium like system (H^-, Li^+, Be^{++}, etc.), for which the nuclear charge is Z, the above procedure leads to the result that the energy is minimised for $Z' = Z - \frac{5}{16}$. The other electron exerts a screening effect of $-\frac{5}{16}$ whatever the nuclear charge. The minimised value of $\bar{E}$, corresponding to that value of Z', is equal to

$$\bar{E} = [-2Z^2 + \tfrac{5}{4}Z - 2(\tfrac{5}{16})^2]E_H. \qquad \text{(VI.13)}$$

Comparison with VI.8 shows that, for all the species, this is $2(\frac{5}{16})^2 E_H = 0.196E_H$ lower than the value obtained by the first order perturbation treatment using the unperturbed wave function. This energy ($-0.196E_H$) may be referred to as a *charge correlation energy*. It is the lowering of the energy resulting from the readjustment of the wave function as a result of the perturbation (electron–electron repulsion). It is surprising that it should be constant for all values of Z. The 'true' charge correlation energy is the difference between the experimental energy and that calculated by first order perturbation theory, because the latter allows accurately for the interaction of the electrons in the *unperturbed* distributions.* This is also surprisingly constant for the species H^- to F^{7+} (see Table III).

TABLE III

Ion	H^-	He	Li^+	Be^{2+}	B^{3+}	C^{4+}	N^{5+}	O^{6+}	F^{7+}
Corr. Energy in units of E_H	0·302	0·308	0·309	0·310	0·312	0·318	0·326	0·338	0·356

This shows that the 'true' correlation energies are about 50%

---

* The term 'correlation' has come to be used for the mutual effect that electrons in a system have on one another's positions in space. This occurs partly as a result of their like charge which causes them to keep apart, and partly, as will be seen later, because of spin effects. The term 'correlation energy' is not always used in the manner described here, but it seems to the author that this is a most profitable definition for the present purpose. The use of E (Hartree) $- E$ (exptal.), which is very common, is unsatisfactory here because E (Hartree) already includes some effects of correlation.

greater than the values obtained by the simple variation treatment already given. However, the suggestion from that treatment that they should be constant is approximately correct.

VI.4 The Hylleraas Treatment of Helium

About 1930 Hylleraas carried out an intensive attack on the ground state of the helium atom. Most of the variation functions he used were of the type

$$e^{-Z'\frac{r_1}{\rho}}.e^{-Z'\frac{r_2}{\rho}}\{1 + f(r_1, r_2, r_{12})\}. \tag{VI.14}$$

For example, one of the simple ones was

$$e^{-Z'\frac{r_1}{\rho}}.e^{-Z'\frac{r_2}{\rho}}\left(1 + C\frac{(r_1 - r_2)^2}{\rho^2}\right). \tag{VI.15}$$

In this function there are two adjustable constants, Z' and C, which were adjusted to minimise the energy. This function gave an energy within 1% of the true value, this being obtained with $Z' = 1\cdot69$ and $C = 0\cdot142$.

However, it is the repulsion between the electrons which causes the electron distribution to be modified. Therefore the most appropriate way of modifying the function would be to introduce a term, or terms, involving r_{12}. Hylleraas tried

$$e^{-Z'\frac{r_1}{\rho}}.e^{-Z'\frac{r_2}{\rho}}\left(1 + C'.\frac{r_{12}}{\rho}\right). \tag{VI.16}$$

With this, the energy was minimised for $Z' = 0\cdot364$ and was within $0\cdot3$ or $0\cdot4\%$ of the true value. This demonstrates the great success attending the inclusion of r_{12}. Unfortunately in this and other problems, including r_{12} in the trial function produces integrals which are more difficult to solve. In molecular problems (except that of H_2) it has not been possible to include r_{12} because the resulting integrals prove to be intractable. This inability to include r_{12}, or anything that is effectively equivalent to it, in functions for any but the most simple systems, must be accounted one of the failures of present-day wave mechanics.

Finally Hylleraas used a function of the form of IV.14 in which the polynomial contained fourteen terms. Each term involved an

adjustable constant and these as well as Z' were adjusted to minimise the energy. The calculated energy was then very close to the
true one. However, very recently Kinoshita (1957) has employed
a function consisting of thirty-nine terms which achieves even
greater success (cf. also Pekeris (1958)). The use of such a complex function is made possible by the advent of high-speed computing machines.

VI.5 The Taylor and Parr Treatment of Helium

This section will be based on a paper by Taylor and Parr (1952),
but other papers by Lennard-Jones (1952), by Mulliken (1952), and
by Lennard-Jones and Pople (1952) use a similar approach. The procedure to be described was investigated by Taylor and Parr, not
because they hoped to calculate a better value for the energy than
had been obtained by Hylleraas, but because they hoped that this
method could be extended more easily to other systems. As just
stated, including terms containing r_{12} in wave functions for systems
other than the helium atom and the hydrogen molecule has not so
far proved practical.

One fault of the simplest variation function $e^{-Z'\frac{r_1}{\rho}} \cdot e^{-Z'\frac{r_2}{\rho}}$ is that
it allows the two electrons independent freedom of movement.
Nothing is included to take account of the tendency of the electrons
to keep apart because of their like charge. Taylor and Parr pointed
out that there would be both a radial correlation, one electron tending to be close to the nucleus and the other farther away, and an
angular correlation, the two electrons tending to be on opposite
sides of the nucleus. Radial correlation will be considered first.

Taylor and Parr suggested that some radial correlation could be
achieved by adding to the $1s^2$ function above $\left(e^{-Z'\frac{r_1}{\rho}} \cdot e^{-Z'\frac{r_2}{\rho}}\right)$, a contribution from a $1s.2s$ function, because a $2s$ function favours the
electron being farther from the nucleus. This function was

$$1s^{Z'}(1) \cdot 1s^{Z'}(2) + a\{1s^{Z'}(1) \cdot 2s^{Z'}(2) + 1s^{Z'}(2) \cdot 2s^{Z'}(1)\}, \quad \text{(VI.17)}$$

where $\qquad\qquad 1s^{Z'}(1) \equiv e^{-\frac{Z'r_1}{\rho}}$ $\qquad\qquad\qquad\qquad$ (VI.18)

and
$$2s^{Z'}(1) \equiv \left(1 - \frac{Z'.r_1}{2\rho}\right)e^{\frac{Z'.r_1}{2\rho}}. \tag{VI.19}$$

The form of the last pair of terms in VI.17 is required by the symmetry of the system, because it is clearly necessary that electrons 1 and 2 should appear in an exactly similar manner to one another. The constants Z' and a were chosen to minimise the energy. The result which shows that there has been a slight improvement in the energy is listed in Table IV. Taylor and Parr added further spherically symmetric s-functions and obtained the results in the first section of Table IV. The improvement is only slight, even with the addition of five extra terms.

TABLE IV

Configurations used	Values of Z		$-\dfrac{E_{calc}}{E_H}$	$\dfrac{E_{calc}-E_{expt}}{E_H}$
$(1s)^2$	1·6875		5·6953	0·1113
$(1s)^2+(1s2s)$	1·757		5·7085	0·0981
$(1s)^2+(1s2s)+(1s3s)$	1·777		5·7117	0·0949
$(1s)^2+(1s2s)+(2s)^2$	1·78		5·7095	0·0971
$(1s)^2+(1s2s)+(1s3s)$ $+(2s)^2+(2s3s)+(3s)^2$	1·764		5·7148	0·0918
$(1s)^2+(2p')^2$	$Z=1·6896$	$Z'=3Z$	5·7387	0·0679
$(1s)^2+(2p')^2+(3d'')^2$	$Z=1·6896$	$Z'=3Z$ $Z''=6Z$	5·7429	0·0637
$(1s)^2+(2p')^2+(3d'')^2$ $+(4f''')^2$	$Z=1·6896$	$Z'=3Z$ $Z''=6Z$ $Z'''=12Z$	5·7438	0·0628
$(1s1s')$	$Z=1·19$	$Z'=1·835Z$	5·7513	0·0552
$(1s1s')+(2p'')^2$	$Z=1·19$	$Z'=1·835Z$ $Z''=4·16Z$	5·7904	0·0162
$(1s1s')+(2p'')^2+(3d''')^2$	$Z=1·19$	$Z'=1·835Z$ $Z''=4·16Z$ $Z'''=9·5Z$	5·7940	0·0125
$(1s1s')+(2p'')^2+(3d''')^2$ $+(4f'''')^2$	$Z=1·19$ $Z'''=9·5Z$	$Z'=1·835Z$ $Z''=4·16Z$ $Z''''=16·0Z$	5·79486	0·0117

The Helium Atom 69

Taylor and Parr allowed for angular correlation by using the angular dependent functions $2p$, etc. For instance the $2p_0$ function contains the factor $\cos \theta$. Therefore the term $(2p)^2$ will contain $\cos \theta_1 \cos \theta_2$. This is positive if θ_1 and θ_2 are equal but negative if, for example, $\theta_1 = \pi + \theta_2$. Therefore if, in

$$(1s)^2 + a(2p')^2, \tag{VI.20}$$

a has a negative sign, the probability for the two electrons being on the same side of the nucleus will be decreased, while that for them being on opposite sides will be increased. When testing functions of the type VI.20, Taylor and Parr varied the 2 parameters for each part separately. The results of this method of allowing for angular correlation are shown in the second section of Table IV. The improvement in the energy is greater than in the first section. This may be so, either because angular is more important than radial correlation, or because the procedure used in the second section of Table IV allows more successfully for angular correlation, than does the procedure in the first section allow for radial correlation.

The first line of the third section of Table IV shows another method of allowing for radial correlation. This function, used by Eckart, is

$$e^{-Z'\frac{r_1}{\rho}}.e^{-Z''\frac{r_2}{\rho}} + e^{-Z'\frac{r_2}{\rho}}.e^{-Z''\frac{r_1}{\rho}}. \tag{VI.21}$$

It implies that the electrons are in two different $1s$ orbitals. The energy is minimised for

$$Z' = 1\cdot19 \qquad Z'' = 1\cdot835 \times Z' = 2\cdot18365. \tag{VI.22}$$

For one electron, the effective nuclear charge is greater than the true one because of the inward directed repulsion of the other, which is in an orbital for which the effective nuclear charge is only slightly greater than unity. That is, the 'inner' electron exerts a very large screening effect. This function allows more effectively for radial correlation than do those of Section 1 of Table IV, the energy obtained using it being much lower than that for even the six-term function of the first section. Taylor and Parr then combined, with this function, the terms that had been used to allow for angular correlation in the second section. The final energy is within $0\cdot2\%$ of the true value.

F

The above systematic approach illustrates a method that will be encountered elsewhere in this book and in the literature. Taylor and Parr used as their basic function either $(1s)^2$ or $(1s1s')$ and then modified them by a judicious admixture of the wave functions of other states; in this case, of excited states. This procedure is known as *configuration interaction*. Each state, $(1s)^2$, $(1s2s)$, $(2p)^2$, etc., is described as a configuration and a better approximation is obtained, in particular for the ground state, by allowing them to interact. The extent of interaction is determined, for the ground state, by using the Variation Theorem and minimising the energy. In other circumstances this procedure has been described as *resonance* with other states, the best approximation that can be achieved being described as a *resonance mixture* of a number of states. There is no essential difference between *configuration interaction* and *resonance*. The method will be successful if a good approximation can be obtained by using only a small number of states. A smaller number will be needed, the more successful is the original choice of the contributing wave functions, or configurations.

Taylor and Parr reached the final conclusion that, for the ground state of helium, angular was more important than radial correlation.

VI.6 The General Problem of Two Electrons

So far, only the two-electron system, in which both the electrons are in the lowest ($1s$) orbital, has been considered. In this section, the wave functions of states for which the electrons are not in the same orbital will be discussed. The discussion will be in terms of the unperturbed wave function, which neglects the effects of interelectron repulsion.

Let the two orbitals that are occupied be designated ψ_A and ψ_B, these being exact solutions of the one-electron problem. Let the energies associated with them be E_A and E_B. For the unperturbed systems $\left(\text{i.e. absence of } \dfrac{e^2}{r_{12}}\right)$, the wave function can be separated, as in the earlier chapter, so that a satisfactory solution of the unperturbed Schrödinger equation is

$$\psi(1, 2) = \psi_A(1) \cdot \psi_B(2). \qquad (VI.23)$$

This formula is consistent with the commonsense conclusion that, if the electrons do not exert any force on one another, the distribution of each will be independent of that of the other. However, the function

$$\psi_A(2).\psi_B(1) \tag{VI.24}$$

is clearly also a satisfactory solution of the Schrödinger equation. Both VI.23 and VI.24 correspond to the same unperturbed energy, namely $E_A + E_B$. That is, VI.23 and VI.24 form a degenerate pair. This state is, at this approximation, doubly degenerate.

In Section III.3 the doubly degenerate solutions for a particle in a ring were discussed. It was shown that, for a doubly degenerate level, the wave functions of the two component states could be chosen in an infinite number of ways. These pairs would be represented by formulae III.17 and III.18, this representation ensuring that the two members of the pairs remained normalised and orthogonal. By analogy in the present case, the pair VI.23 and VI.24 could be replaced by

$$\cos\alpha.\psi_A(1).\psi_B(2) + \sin\alpha.\psi_A(2).\psi_B(1), \tag{VI.25}$$

and $\quad -\sin\alpha.\psi_A(1).\psi_B(2) + \cos\alpha.\psi_A(2).\psi_B(1), \tag{VI.26}$

which correspond to an infinite number of possibilities since α can be assigned any value.

So far our only concern has been that the wave functions should satisfy the Schrödinger equation without the perturbation. This all pairs of the form of VI.25 and VI.26 do. However, another feature must be considered, which is that the electrons are indistinguishable from one another. It is a further postulate of wave mechanics that this indistinguishability is a fundamental and unassailable property of electrons and not merely a consequence of a human lack of skill. This means that the probability (ψ^2) for a configuration in which one electron is at position a and the other at position b must always be equal to the probability of the configuration in which the electrons are interchanged. This may be represented by

$$\{\psi(1, 2)\}^2 = \{\psi(2, 1)\}^2. \tag{VI.27}$$

It follows that

$$\psi(1, 2) = +\psi(2, 1), \tag{VI.28}$$

or $\qquad\qquad\qquad\qquad -\psi(2, 1). \tag{VI.29}$

This additional requirement means that only one pair of VI.25 and VI.26 is allowed. The coefficients of all terms in these two formulae must have the same absolute magnitude. Therefore the only allowable pair is

$$\psi_s = \frac{1}{\sqrt{2}}\psi_A(1).\psi_B(2) + \frac{1}{\sqrt{2}}\psi_A(2).\psi_B(1), \qquad \text{(VI.30)}$$

$$\psi_a = \frac{1}{\sqrt{2}}\psi_A(1).\psi_B(2) - \frac{1}{\sqrt{2}}\psi_A(2).\psi_B(1). \qquad \text{(VI.31)}$$

The function VI.30 has the property VI.28, and VI.31 has the property VI.29, as may be seen by interchanging the numbers, which represent the electrons, in VI.30 and VI.31. Because VI.30 has the property VI.28 it is said to be *symmetric* to the interchange of electrons, while VI.31, having the property VI.29, is said to be *antisymmetric* to the interchange of electrons.

The functions VI.30 and VI.31 correspond to two states which are degenerate for the unperturbed problem. However, they will not necessarily remain degenerate under the action of the perturbation which is, in this case, inter-electron repulsion. In Chapter II, Section 5, for the particle in a cubic box, the perturbation examined destroyed the degeneracy of a group of states. The states corresponding to VI.30 and VI.31 will only remain degenerate under the action of the perturbation if, for both, the spatial configuration of the electrons is identical. It will be shown, for a particular example, that the spatial configuration is *not* the same for the symmetric VI.30 and the antisymmetric VI.31.

The helium atom having one electron in the $1s$ (A) and the other in the $2s$ (B) orbital will be used as an example:

$$\psi_A = N_1.e^{-2\frac{r}{\rho}} \qquad \text{(VI.32)}$$

and

$$\psi_B = N_2\left(1 - \frac{r}{\rho}\right).e^{-\frac{r}{\rho}}. \qquad \text{(VI.33)}$$

(These follow from IV.24 and IV.27, the effect of increasing the nuclear charge to 2 being to replace $\frac{r}{\rho}$ in hydrogen by $\frac{2r}{\rho}$ in He+.)

The corresponding orbitals for the hydrogen atom were shown graphically in Figure 6, and the probability patterns of two kinds (P_u and P_r) in Figures 7 and 8. The curves for VI.32 and VI.33 are the same except for a change of scale; the $\frac{r}{\rho}$ scale must be halved $\left(\text{i.e. the point } \frac{r}{\rho} = 2 \text{ for H must be labelled } \frac{r}{\rho} = 1 \text{ for He}^+\right)$.

For this example

$$\psi_s = N_1 N_2 \left\{ e^{-2\frac{r_1}{\rho}} \cdot \left(1 - \frac{r_2}{\rho}\right) e^{-\frac{r_2}{\rho}} + e^{-2\frac{r_2}{\rho}} \cdot \left(1 - \frac{r_1}{\rho}\right) e^{-\frac{r_1}{\rho}} \right\}, \quad \text{(VI.34)}$$

and

$$\psi_a = N_1 N_2 \left\{ e^{-2\frac{r_1}{\rho}} \cdot \left(1 - \frac{r_2}{\rho}\right) e^{-\frac{r_2}{\rho}} - e^{-2\frac{r_2}{\rho}} \cdot \left(1 - \frac{r_1}{\rho}\right) e^{-\frac{r_1}{\rho}} \right\}. \quad \text{(VI.35)}$$

The wave function and the probabilities are functions of only two coordinates, r_1 and r_2, both orbitals being spherically symmetric. Therefore the probabilities can be represented by contour diagrams as a function of the positions of the electrons, r_1 and r_2. This is done in Figures 10a and 10b, which show P_r, the probability of finding the electron at a radius r (not the probability per unit volume). The contours are, therefore, for $4\pi r_1^2 . 4\pi r_2^2 . \psi_s^2$ in 10a and for $4\pi r_1^2 . 4\pi r_2^2 . \psi_a^2$ in 10b (cf. Section IV.3).

The contour diagrams in Figures 10a and 10b are quite different. For the symmetric state, there is a maximum of the probability surface for both electrons at about $\frac{r}{\rho} = \frac{1}{2}$ For the antisymmetric state, the probability of finding the two electrons at the same radius is always zero. This follows from the form of VI.31 from which it is clear that, if the two electrons are at the same place, the two terms are equal and, because of the negative sign, ψ_a is zero. In the present example, the wave functions are dependent on r only, but it is apparent that, for all antisymmetric states, the electrons will have a zero probability of being at the same place, and a low probability of being near one another. This does not apply for the symmetric case. To demonstrate this, the configurations of zero probability are shown by dotted lines in Figures 10a and 10b.

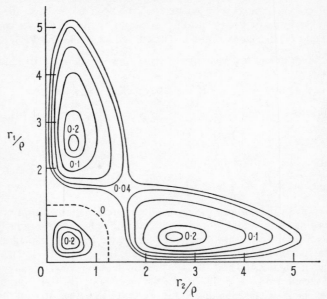

Fig. 10a. Contour diagrams of the probability of electron 1 being at r_1, and electron 2 at r_2 for the helium atom in the $1s.2s$ state: (a) For ψ_s, singlet.

At the beginning of this section it was stated that VI.23 was consistent with the commonsense conclusion that, if there is no force between the electrons, the distribution of each will be independent of that of the other. This *commonsense conclusion* has now to be modified as Figure 10 indicates that for one of the two states arising from the occupation of the $1s$ and $2s$ orbitals the electrons tend to keep apart, while for the other there is no such tendency to keep apart but there is some tendency for them to be drawn together (Dickens and Linnett (1957)). This does *not* arise from a *force* between the particles, for the functions considered are for the unperturbed problem. It is a consequence of the form required for the wave functions because the electrons are indistinguishable.

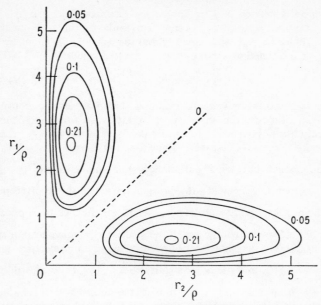

Fig. 10b, (b), For ψ_a, triplet. (Relative values of probabilities, nodes are shown by broken lines)

The energies of these two states, as obtained by the application of the perturbation method, will be discussed in the next section but one, after the significance of electron spin in this context has been examined.

VI.7 Electron Spin and the Pauli Principle

Magnetic experiments, such as those of Stern and Gerlach (1923), and spectral observations, such as that of the doublet character of the *D* line of sodium, can be interpreted by supposing that the electron has an intrinsic magnetic moment. Because it is charged, this magnetic moment is accounted for by ascribing to the particle a *spin*. The nature of the results (e.g. the fact that the *D* line of sodium consists of two sharp lines and only two) requires that, when a

direction is defined, say by applying a magnetic field, the axis of
spin can only take up two orientations with respect to that direction. The numerical results require that the spin angular momentum
about the selected axis can only have the two values

$$+ \frac{1}{2} \cdot \frac{h}{2\pi} \quad \text{and} \quad - \frac{1}{2} \cdot \frac{h}{2\pi}. \tag{VI.36}$$

It is only necessary here to examine the inter-relation between
electron spin and the spatial part of the wave function. Consequently it is not necessary to specify the form of the wave function,
but only to suppose that there is one function α, associated with the
state for which the resolved part of the angular momentum is $+ \frac{1}{2} \cdot \frac{h}{2\pi}$,
and another β, associated with the state for which the resolved part
of the angular momentum is $- \frac{1}{2} \cdot \frac{h}{2\pi}$. It will further be supposed
that, for a two-electron system, if the resultant spin angular momen-
tum of a state is zero, it is only possible to say that one electron has a
spin of $+ \frac{1}{2} \cdot \frac{h}{2\pi}$ and the other a spin of $- \frac{1}{2} \cdot \frac{h}{2\pi}$; it is not possible to
say *which* electron has *which* spin momentum. This is a natural
extension of the postulate of electron-indistinguishability.

For two electrons 1 and 2, there are therefore four possibilities
for the total spin wave function:

$$\alpha(1) . \alpha(2), \tag{VI.37}$$

$$\beta(1) . \beta(2), \tag{VI.38}$$

$$\frac{1}{\sqrt{2}}\alpha(1) . \beta(2) + \frac{1}{\sqrt{2}}\alpha(2) . \beta(1). \tag{VI.39}$$

$$\frac{1}{\sqrt{2}}\alpha(1) . \beta(2) - \frac{1}{\sqrt{2}}\alpha(2) . \beta(1). \tag{VI.40}$$

The last two are required to have the above form by arguments
identical with those used in arriving at VI.30 and VI.31. The first
of the above functions, VI.37, corresponds to a resultant spin angular
momentum about the prescribed axis of $+1\frac{h}{2\pi}$, the second, VI.38,

to $-1\frac{h}{2\pi}$ and the third and fourth, VI.39 and VI.40, to a zero resultant spin angular momentum about that axis.

Of the above four functions, the first three are symmetric to the interchange of electrons, as may be seen by interchanging the numbers 1 and 2, while the last is antisymmetric to such an interchange.

It will be supposed that the interaction between the spin and orbital motion is negligible. The wave function can then be separated into a spin part and an orbital part, the total spin-orbital wave function being a product of the two parts. For the case in which there are two electrons in the orbitals A and B, there are clearly eight possibilities for, in principle, each of the two spatial functions VI. 30 and VI. 31 could be multiplied by each of the four spin functions VI.37 to VI.40. Those products which are made up of a symmetric space function and a symmetric spin function, and those which are made up of an antisymmetric space function and an antisymmetric spin function, will be symmetric; while those for which one part is symmetric and the other antisymmetric will be antisymmetric.

According to the *Pauli Principle*, in its wave mechanical form, *the total wave function must be antisymmetric to the interchange of electrons*. This is a further postulate; it cannot be proved except by the success of the conclusions drawn from it. The Pauli Principle is of the most far-reaching importance in Chemistry.

Therefore of the eight wave functions that are obtained by multiplying VI.30 and VI.31 by VI.37 to VI.40, only four are permitted by the Pauli Principle. These are:

$$\left[\frac{1}{\sqrt{2}}\psi_A(1).\psi_B(2) + \frac{1}{\sqrt{2}}\psi_A(2).\psi_B(1)\right]$$
$$\left[\frac{1}{\sqrt{2}}\alpha(1).\beta(2) - \frac{1}{\sqrt{2}}\alpha(2).\beta(1)\right] \quad \text{(VI.41)}$$

$$\left[\frac{1}{\sqrt{2}}\psi_A(1).\psi_B(2) - \frac{1}{\sqrt{2}}\psi_A(2).\psi_B(1)\right]\left[\alpha(1).\alpha(2)\right] \quad \text{(VI.42)}$$

$$\left[\frac{1}{\sqrt{2}}\psi_A(1).\psi_B(2) - \frac{1}{\sqrt{2}}\psi_A(2).\psi_B(1)\right]\left[\beta(1).\beta(2)\right] \quad \text{(VI.43)}$$

$$\left[\frac{1}{\sqrt{2}}\psi_A(1).\psi_B(2) - \frac{1}{\sqrt{2}}\psi_A(2).\psi_B(1)\right]$$
$$\left[\frac{1}{\sqrt{2}}\alpha(1).\beta(2) + \frac{1}{\sqrt{2}}\alpha(2).\beta(1)\right]. \quad \text{(VI.44)}$$

The symmetric space wave function is associated with one spin function for which the resultant spin angular momentum along a prescribed direction is zero. The antisymmetric space wave function is associated with three spin functions for which the resultant spin angular momenta along a prescribed direction are $+1\frac{h}{2\pi}$, $-1\frac{h}{2\pi}$ and zero. The above functions are therefore interpreted in the following way. The symmetric space wave function is associated with a zero spin angular momentum; that is, the spins of the two electrons are opposed. The antisymmetric space wave function is associated with a total spin angular momentum of $1\frac{h}{2\pi}$, which can have the resolved values about the prescribed direction of $+1\frac{h}{2\pi}$, $-1\frac{h}{2\pi}$ and zero; that is, the spins of the two electrons are parallel. Therefore, if the two electrons have parallel spins, the space wave function is antisymmetric, while, if they have opposed spins, the space wave function is symmetric. Reference to Figures 10a and 10b, and the discussion of them, shows that, as regards spatial distribution, if the electrons have parallel spins, there is a tendency for them to keep apart, while, if they have opposed spins, there is a tendency for them to be drawn together.* This is not an effect derived from a force, in the ordinary sense of the word, that the electrons exert on one another, for, in the unperturbed situation with which we are dealing, the potential energy is not dependent on the distance between the electrons. This effect is a consequence of the fundamental indistinguishability of electrons and of the Pauli Principle.

How does the above statement of the Pauli Principle link up

---

* It would strictly be more correct to present this in terms of the symmetry of the spin wave functions VI 37 to VI 40, but since chemists are used to thinking in terms of electrons spins being parallel or opposed, this form is used here.

with the more widely known one, which is that, in an atom, no two electrons can have all four quantum numbers the same? In the example just considered, the assignment of the two electrons to two different spatial orbitals, A and B, would mean, in an atomic system, that the two orbitals would differ as regards at least one of the quantum numbers (k, l and m). Consequently the spin quantum numbers can be the same (e.g. both $+\frac{1}{2}$) or different ($+\frac{1}{2}$ and $-\frac{1}{2}$). Let us consider the situation when both electrons occupy the same orbital, say A. The space wave function is then

$$\psi = \psi_A(1).\psi_A(2). \tag{VI.45}$$

This is symmetric to the interchange of electrons. Therefore in forming the total spin orbital function, the Pauli Principle requires that it can combine only with the single antisymmetric spin function VI.44. This spin function corresponds to the resultant total spin angular momentum being zero; that is, to opposed spins and to different spin quantum numbers, $+\frac{1}{2}$ and $-\frac{1}{2}$. Therefore, if all the spatial quantum numbers are the same, the wave mechanical form of the Pauli Principle requires that the spin quantum numbers shall be different. The wave mechanical form of the Pauli Principle leads, as a special case, to the form that is better known to chemists. However, the wave mechanical form of the Pauli Principle has additional implications which are of the greatest importance in Chemistry. These are the mutual effects that electrons have on one another's spatial distributions, the effects being dependent on whether the spins are opposed or parallel.

Because there is a magnetic interaction between spin and orbital motions the three states VI.42, VI.43 and VI.44 may not have the same energy. Therefore this group forms a triplet. When the magnetic interactions are small, as they are for helium, the splitting between the members of the triplet is small. The other state, VI.41, is a singlet. Consequently the states arising from the occupation by two electrons of two different orbitals (e.g. $1s$ and $2s$ in helium), are a triplet for which the electrons' spins are parallel, and a singlet for which they are opposed. When the electrons are in the same orbital, there is only a singlet because the spins must be opposed. In the next section the difference in energy between singlet and triplet states will be examined.

VI.8 Coulomb and Spin Correlation or Exchange Energy

In this section, the perturbation method will be applied to the singlet and triplet states arising from the occupation by two electrons of a given pair of atomic orbitals, A and B. The perturbation is the repulsion between the electrons, ψ_A and ψ_B being the normalised solutions for the unperturbed system. Application of the formula V.8 to the functions VI.30 and VI.31 leads to:

$$E' = \int \int \frac{e^2}{r_{12}} \left\{ \frac{1}{\sqrt{2}} \psi_A(1) \cdot \psi_B(2) \pm \frac{1}{\sqrt{2}} \psi_A(2) \cdot \psi_B(1) \right\}^2 d\tau_1 \, d\tau_2, \quad \text{(VI.46)}$$

where E' is the perturbation energy. Since

$$\int \int \frac{e^2}{r_{12}} \{ \psi_A(1) \cdot \psi_B(2) \}^2 \, d\tau_1 \, d\tau_2$$

$$= \int \int \frac{e^2}{r_{12}} \{ \psi_A(2) \cdot \psi_B(1) \}^2 \, d\tau_1 \, d\tau_2, \quad \text{(VI.47)}$$

$$E' = \int \int \frac{e^2}{r_{12}} \{ (\psi_A(1))^2 \cdot (\psi_B(2))^2 \} \, d\tau_1 \, d\tau_2$$

$$\pm \int \int \frac{e^2}{r_{12}} \{ (\psi_A(1) \cdot \psi_B(1))(\psi_A(2) \cdot \psi_B(2)) \} d\tau_1 \, d\tau_2 \quad \text{(VI.48)}$$

$$= C \pm K, \quad \text{(VI.49)}$$

where

$$\int \int \frac{e^2}{r_{12}} \{ (\psi_A(1))^2 \cdot (\psi_B(2))^2 \} d\tau_1 \, d\tau_2 = C \quad \text{(VI.50)}$$

and

$$\int \int \frac{e^2}{r_{12}} \{ (\psi_A(1) \cdot \psi_B(1))(\psi_A(2) \cdot \psi_B(2)) \} d\tau_1 \, d\tau_2 = K. \quad \text{(VI.51)}$$

The integral in VI.50 is described as a coulomb integral, and C is called the coulomb energy. The integral in VI.51 has been described as an exchange integral, and K is usually called the exchange energy. In this case both C and K are positive.

The coulomb energy C is simply the mean interaction of one electron in orbital A with another in orbital B. The exchange energy cannot be explained in such simple terms. In fact the term exchange energy is an unfortunate choice, though not an unnatural one. K is really a spin correlation energy. For the triplet state, having the antisymmetric spatial wave function, the perturbation energy is $(C - K)$. The coulomb energy, C, measures the interaction that would exist if there were no effects arising from the indistinguishability of electrons and the Pauli Principle. The exchange energy, K, measures the lowering of the energy resulting from the tendency of the electrons having the same spin to keep apart by virtue of spin correlation. Therefore K should in this case more properly be described as a *spin correlation energy*. For the singlet state having the symmetric wave function the perturbation energy is $C + K$. Here the electrons have opposed spins and tend to come together, so that the spin correlation energy, in this case, leads to a further increase in the energy over and above that arising from the simple coulomb interaction.

For the $1s2s$ state of helium, the unperturbed energy of this state is $-5E_H$, the sum of the energies of an electron in a $1s$ state of He^+ ($-4E_H$) and one in a $2s$ state of He^+ ($-E_H$). The coulomb energy is $0.839E_H$ and K is $0.088E_H$. Therefore the energy of the singlet state is calculated to be $-4.073E_H$ and that of the triplet state $-4.249E_H$. The experimental energies are $-4.293E_H$ and $-4.351E_H$. There is an additional lowering because the orbitals are modified by the repulsion between the electrons. This may therefore be regarded as a *charge correlation energy*. For the singlet state it is $-0.220E_H$, while for the triplet it is $-0.102E_H$. The charge correlation energy is greater for the singlet than the triplet because, in the former state, the spin correlation has brought the electrons together, while, in the latter, it has 'forced' them apart.

For states in which the two electrons are in the same orbit, the perturbation method gives

$$E' = \int \int \frac{e^2}{r_{12}} \{(\psi_A(1))^2 . (\psi_A(2))^2\} d\tau_1 \, d\tau_2 \qquad \text{(VI.52)}$$
$$= C.$$

In this case there is no 'exchange' or 'spin correlation' energy, since there is no exchange or spin correlation. So that, for this state, the coulomb energy is $2.5E_H$, the spin correlation energy zero, and the charge correlation energy $-0.308E_H$ (cf. Table III). It would be expected that the charge correlation energy would be greater for the $1s^2$ state of helium than for either of the $1s2s$ states, because the electrons are in the same orbital and hence, on an average, closer together, so that their repulsion has a greater effect. Moreover, the $1s$ orbital is more concentrated spatially than the $2s$.

The same procedure that was carried out for the $1s2s$ states of helium may be applied to the $1s2p$ state. The coulomb energy (C) is $0.971E_H$ while the spin correlation energy (K) is $0.068\ E_H$. Therefore the calculated energies of the singlet and triplet states are $-3.961E_H$ and $-4.097\ E_H$ respectively. This implies that the singlet state should be unstable with respect to ionisation to He^+ for the lowest energy of He^+ is $-4E_H$. This is not so, the experimental energies of the singlet and triplet states being $-4.247E_H$ and $-4.265E_H$. The charge correlation energies are therefore $-0.286E_H$ and $-0.168E_H$ for the singlet and triplet states respectively. These results are compared with the results for the $1s2s$

TABLE V

	Singlet				Triplet			
	C	Spin corr.	Charge corr.	Total	C	Spin corr.	Charge corr.	Total
$1s2s$	$+0.839$	$+0.088$	-0.220	$+0.707$	$+0.839$	-0.088	-0.102	$+0.649$
$1s2p$	$+0.971$	$+0.068$	-0.286	$+0.753$	$+0.921$	-0.068	-0.168	$+0.735$

states in Table V. The main reason why the $1s2s$ state is lower than the $1s2p$ state is that the coulomb integral, C, is lower for the $1s2s$ state than for the $1s2p$. Since the breakdown of the degeneracy of the ns, np, nd, etc., orbitals in polyelectronic atoms, and the fact that the electrons in the ns orbital are the most tightly bound, are of great interest to the chemist the reasons for this difference between the two coulomb integrals will be considered in more detail.

This is most effectively examined by making use of the probabilities which have been labelled P_r (Section IV.3). These are the probabilities of finding the electron at a radius r, and are equal to $4\pi r^2 . \psi^2$.

For the $1s$ state of helium $\psi = N_1 e^{-\frac{2r}{\rho}}$, and P_r is a maximum at $r = \frac{\rho}{2}$. For the $2s$ state $\psi = N_2\left(1 - \frac{r}{\rho}\right)e^{-\frac{r}{\rho}}$ and P_r is a maximum at

$r = 0.38\rho$ and at 2.62ρ, the outer maximum being much the larger

(cf. Figure 8). For the $2p$ states $\psi = N_2' \cdot \dfrac{r}{\rho} \cdot e^{-\frac{r}{\rho}}$ and P_r is a maximum

at $r = 2\rho$. Because the main maximum for the $2p$ orbital is at a smaller value of r than for the $2s$ orbital, the average distance between the electrons is less when one is in a $1s$ and one in a $2p$ orbital, than when one is in a $1s$ and one in a $2s$ orbital. Therefore the value of the coulomb energy is greater for the $1s2p$ than for the $1s2s$ states.

It is more difficult to reach a satisfactory conclusion about the spin correlation energies (K), because they seem more nebulous at the present time, and hence are more difficult to assess. However, the value of K is dependent on the behaviour of the product $\psi_A \cdot \psi_B$ (cf. VI.49 and VI.51). For the $1s2s$ states $4\pi r^2 \psi_{1s} \cdot \psi_{2s}$ has its maxima at $r = 0.42\rho$ and $r = 1.58\rho$ while for the $1s2p$ states $4\pi r^2 \psi_{1s} \cdot \psi_{2p}$ has its maximum at $r = 3\rho$. Because the main maximum of the former occurs at a much smaller radius, and therefore inter-electronic distances have a higher probability of being smaller, the spin correlation energy K is bigger for the $1s2s$ states than for the $1s2p$ states.

The charge correlation effects are greater for the $1s2s$ states than for the $1s2p$ states. This is to be expected, because the coulomb integrals are greater. If the mean repulsion energy between the two electron distributions is greater, then more gain in energy can presumably be achieved by a given distortion. Reference to Table V shows that, for the $1s2p$ states, as for the $1s2s$ states, the charge correlation energy is much greater for the singlet than for the triplet state. The reason for this was discussed for the $1s2s$ states. The same reason must apply to the $1s2p$ states and, in fact, to all pairs of singlet and triplet states.

In Table III it was shown that the charge correlation energies for the $1s^2$ states of helium and the analogous two-electron ions from H^- to F^{7+} were surprisingly constant. Table VI gives similar results for the $1s2p$ states of the two electron species from He to F^{7+}. As for the $1s^2$ state, the charge correlation energies are surprisingly constant. For the $1s^2$ states, the variation was about 15% from He to F^{7+}. For both the singlets and triplets in Table VI, it is less than 10%. That the charge correlation energy should be nearly as great for the singlet $1s2p$ states as for the $1s^2$ states is, at first sight, surprising. The explanation may lie, in part, in the fact that, in the $1s^2$ states, the electrons have a high probability of being close together because they are in the same orbital, while in the singlet $1s2p$ state they are brought together by spin correlation. However, this cannot be the whole explanation because the coulomb energy is much greater for the $1s^2$ states than for the singlet $1s2p$ states. It must be that, in addition, the orbits in the $1s2p$ states are more easily distorted by inter-electron repulsion. This would be expected

TABLE VI

	Singlet				Triplet			
	C	Spin corr.	Charge corr.	Total	C	Spin corr.	Charge corr.	Total
He	0·971	+0·068	−0·287	+0·752	0·971	−0·068	−0·168	+0·735
Li$^+$	1·456	+0·102	−0·294	+1·264	1·456	−0·102	−0·158	+1·196
Be^{2+}	1·944	+0·137	−0·302	+1·779	1·944	−0·137	−0·158	+1·649
B^{3+}	2·428	+0·171	−0·303	+2·296	2·428	−0·171	−0·153	+2·104
C^{4+}	2·912	+0·205	−0·307	+2·810	2·912	−0·205	−0·153	+2·554
N^{5+}	3·400	+0·239	−0·310	+3·329	3·400	−0·239	−0·154	+3·007
O^{6+}	3·884	+0·273	−0·311	+3·846	3·884	−0·273	−0·153	+3·458
F^{7+}	4·372	+0·307	−0·316	+4·363	4·372	−0·307	−0·156	+3·909

since the $2p$ orbitals are more extensive than the $1s$ orbitals. Undoubtedly the $1s2p$ state would be more polarisable than the $1s^2$ state.

Before concluding this discussion of the energies of various states of the helium atom, it is important to examine the nature of the various energy terms that have been used. The division of the energy of any system into separate parts is, of necessity, an arbitrary procedure, and therefore the nature of the division should always be scrutinised. The coulomb energy, C, is solely potential energy and arises from the term $\dfrac{e^2}{r_{12}}$ which appears in the integral. The spin correlation energy is likewise solely potential energy, since it also arises from the term $\dfrac{e^2}{r_{12}}$ which appears in the integral, K; it is a *modification* of the coulomb potential energy, this modification being a result of the effect of the operation of the Pauli Principle on the mutual positions of the electrons. The charge correlation term, on the other hand, includes both electronic kinetic energy and potential energy terms. The kinetic energy terms arise because the modification of the wave function, resulting from the repulsion between the electrons, will affect the *curvature* of the wave function; that is, the kinetic energy. The potential energy terms are of two types, for nuclear–electron interactions are modified as well as electron–electron interaction. Since the charge correlation energy is made up of so many parts it is perhaps particularly surprising that it remains so constant from He to F^{7+}. A reason for this may lie in a compensation between the potential and kinetic energy parts. Finally, it is worth stressing that, whatever arbitrary terms are used for a discussion of the electronic energy, it is made up of potential energy and the wave mechanical equivalent of kinetic energy.

VI.9 Hund's Rule and Russell–Saunders Coupling

Hund's rule, as applied to two electrons, states that, for the two states arising when two electrons occupy different orbitals, A and B, the triplet state will be lower in energy than the singlet. This rule is a direct consequence of spin correlation, the electrons with parallel spin tending to keep apart and those with opposed spins tending to be drawn together, so that the spin correlation energy is negative for the triplet and positive for the singlet. Because this behaviour follows very clearly from the Pauli Principle, the rule has very few exceptions. It only fails when special interactions between states occur so that the simple statement that two states arise from the occupation of orbitals A and B is a very much oversimplified one.

Russell–Saunders Coupling, which operates for atoms of low atomic number, can be applied to two electron systems in the following way. If the two electrons occupy two orbitals having total

orbital angular momenta of $\sqrt{l_1(l_1 + 1)}\,\dfrac{h}{2\pi}$ and $\sqrt{l_2(l_2 + 1)}\,\dfrac{h}{2\pi}$, then

G

states having different resultant total orbital angular momenta will have very different energies (coupling is strong) and states which have different total spin angular momenta (spins opposed or spins parallel) will have very different energies (coupling is strong); on the other hand, states which have the same resultant orbital and resultant spin angular momenta, but involve different orientations of them with respect to one another, do not differ greatly in energy (coupling is weak).

Suppose two electrons occupied orbitals $n_1 p$ and $n_2 p$. They could both occupy p_{+1} orbitals, in which case the resultant orbital angular momentum would correspond to $L = 2$. Or one might occupy p_{+1} and the other p_0, when the resultant would be $L = 1$. However, these two pairs of orbitals would be differently disposed relative to one another in space. (This may be visualised by thinking of the pair p_x and p_x, and the pair p_x and p_z.) Therefore the coulomb energies of the two states, having different resultant angular momenta, will be different. Since coulomb energies which depend on inter-electron repulsion are large in atomic systems, the energy difference would be large. As regards the effect of the resultant spin angular momentum, the energy difference will be considerable, because the states differ in the mutual alignment of the electron spins and therefore they differ in spin correlation. The spin correlation energy is considerable because it arises from inter-electron repulsion. On the other hand the interaction of spin and orbital angular momenta is a magnetic interaction, and, for atoms of low atomic number, the energy of this interaction is small. Consequently the *three* states arising by multiplying the antisymmetric orbital wave function by the *three* spin wave functions (VI.37, 38, 39) are very close together. Therefore Russell–Saunders coupling operates in atoms for which the electron repulsion energies are large compared with the energies of magnetic interactions. This is so for elements of low atomic number. As the atomic number increases, the magnetic interactions become relatively more important, so that ultimately the Russell–Saunders approximation breaks down, and other systems have to be adopted which take account of the greater importance of magnetic interactions.

VI.10 Conclusion

In this chapter a further most important postulate of wave mechanics has been introduced, namely the Pauli Principle. The existence of electron 'spin' has also been taken into account, and it has been shown that the Pauli Principle and electron spin together have a profound effect on the electron distribution in systems containing two electrons. Because of this, and of electron interaction, the Pauli Principle and electron spin have an important effect on the energies of such systems. This effect has been examined by making use of the approximate methods described in the last chapter. This has led to the terms *coulomb energy* and *spin correlation energy*. By considering experimental energies, the term *charge correlation energy* has been introduced. Spin and charge correlation energies result from the modification of the electron distribution because of the Pauli Principle and the indistinguishability of electrons, and because of interelectron repulsion.

In this chapter, the term 'spin correlation energy' has been used to replace the term 'exchange energy', because it describes better the effect on which that energy term depends. The term exchange energy is based more directly on the form of the integral, which gives the value of the energy. It will be found, in the next chapter, that the term exchange energy has been used for a term in the calculated energy of the hydrogen molecule even though that term takes account of a quite different effect. It seems better, therefore, to modify the terminology and to use 'spin correlation energy' for K.

CHAPTER VII

The Hydrogen Molecule

VII.1 Introduction

In this chapter some of the treatments of the hydrogen molecule ion, H_2^+, and the hydrogen molecule, H_2, will be described. The former is included because it introduces the problems arising when the electron is subjected to the effect of two nuclei, but the additional problems that arise because of inter-electron repulsion and correlation are absent.

There have been many treatments of the hydrogen molecule; not all can be mentioned here. In particular those treatments which form the basis of procedures that have been extended to more complex molecular systems will be described. The most important are the *valence bond* and *molecular orbital* methods, which differ in their approach to the problem of constructing trial wave functions for the molecular system. For making calculations of energies and other properties in molecular systems, the fundamental problem is how to choose the approximate wave function. It is not unfair to say that no method has been discovered for constructing really satisfactory trial functions for molecular systems other than hydrogen. As a consequence, it is not yet possible to make *a priori* calculations for chemically interesting molecules other than hydrogen, in order to obtain accurate and reliable values of physical properties which are of undoubted use to the chemist. This difficulty arises because functions which would give accurate results are too complicated to be handled by the procedures of Chapter V, while those which can be handled in a reasonable time by those methods are not sufficiently good to give reliable numerical results. It is therefore worth while to examine the different methods when applied to the hydrogen molecule, so that their merits and faults can more easily be assessed.

It must be stressed that the gloomy statement of the last paragraph applies only to the *a priori* calculation of molecular properties by wave mechanics. The success of wave mechanics in providing new concepts and in increasing our qualitative understanding of such phenomena as directed valency has been very great. Also there are many profitable semi-empirical applications of wave mechanics in which either different properties of the same molecule, or one or more properties of a number of molecules, are interconnected.

VII.2 The Hydrogen Molecule Ion

The application of wave mechanics to molecules is an electronic problem. That is, calculations are made for an electronic wave function with the nuclei fixed at a particular configuration; in this case, at a particular internuclear distance R. To obtain the complete potential energy curve, separate calculations must be made for a number of values of R. With complicated wave functions, however, this would often involve so much labour, that calculations are only made for the known equilibrium internuclear distance, as it is for this configuration that the physical properties are known experimentally.

The hydrogen molecule ion has a dissociation energy (D_e) of $2 \cdot 791$ eV and the equilibrium internuclear distance (r_e) is $1 \cdot 060$ Å. The total energy, relative to two nuclei and one electron infinitely separated, is therefore $-16 \cdot 386$ eV or $-1 \cdot 205 E_H$, so that the dissociation energy is only a smallish part of the total electronic energy.

The two nuclei will be labelled A and B. If they are well separated there are two possible ground states of the system, $H_A + H_B^+$ and $H_A^+ + H_B$, which are degenerate. The normalised wave function of the first is $N_1 e^{-\frac{r_A}{\rho}} (1s_A)$, where r_A is the distance from the electron to nucleus A, and that of the second is $N_1 e^{-\frac{r_B}{\rho}} (1s_B)$. As the nuclei are brought together, it is clearly inappropriate to use either one of these alone, but a possible trial function that suggests itself is to combine them with equal weight giving:

$$\psi = 1s_A + 1s_B. \tag{VII.1}$$

The positive sign is used so that VII.1 has no node. The combination with a negative sign would have a central planar nodal surface and therefore a higher energy.

The Hamiltonian H for the hydrogen molecule ion is:

$$H = -\frac{h^2}{8\pi^2 m}\nabla^2 - \frac{e^2}{r_A} - \frac{e^2}{r_B} + \frac{e^2}{R}. \qquad (VII.2)$$

The mean energy corresponding to VII.1 may be calculated by the methods of Chapter V. The formula is:

$$\bar{E} = \frac{\displaystyle\int (1s_A + 1s_B).H.(1s_A + 1s_B)\,d\tau}{\displaystyle\int (1s_A + 1s_B)^2\,d\tau}$$

$$= \frac{\displaystyle\int 1s_A.H.1s_A\,d\tau + \int 1s_A.H.1s_B\,d\tau}{1 + \displaystyle\int 1s_A\,1s_B\,d\tau}, \qquad (VII.3)$$

since, by symmetry,

$$\int 1s_A.H.1s_A\,d\tau = \int 1s_B.H.1s_B\,d\iota, \qquad (VII.4)$$

$$\int 1s_A.H.1s_B\,d\tau = \int 1s_B.H.1s_A\,d\tau, \qquad (VII.5)$$

and

$$\int 1s_A.1s_A\,d\tau = \int 1s_B.1s_B\,d\tau = 1. \qquad (VII.6)$$

The following symbols will be used:

$$H_{aa} = \int 1s_A.H.1s_A\,d\tau, \qquad (VII.7)$$

$$H_{ab} = \int 1s_A.H.1s_B\,d\tau, \qquad (VII.8)$$

and

$$S = \int 1s_A.1s_B\,d\tau. \qquad (VII.9)$$

As regards VII.7, the first two terms of H (VII.2) will lead to $-E_H$
the last term to $\dfrac{e^2}{R}$ for nuclear repulsion and the third term, which
is the interaction of the electron distribution on A with the nucleus
B, equals

$$- \int 1s_A . \frac{e^2}{r_B} . 1s_A \, d\tau = \left\{ e^{-\frac{2R}{\rho}} \left(1 + \frac{\rho}{R} \right) - \frac{\rho}{R} \right\} \frac{e^2}{\rho}. \quad \text{(VII.10)}$$

As regards VII.8 this is equal to:

$$\left(-E_H + \frac{e^2}{R} \right) S - \int 1s_A . \frac{e^2}{r_A} . 1s_B \, d\tau$$

$$= \left(-E_H + \frac{e^2}{R} \right) S - \left\{ \left(\frac{R}{\rho} + 1 \right) e^{-\frac{R}{\rho}} \right\} \frac{e^2}{\rho}. \quad \text{(VII.11)}$$

The integral S in VII.9 is called the overlap integral and is given by

$$S = \left(1 + \frac{R}{\rho} + \frac{R^2}{3\rho^2} \right) e^{-\frac{R}{\rho}}. \quad \text{(VII.12)}$$

Therefore the energy is

$$\bar{E} = -E_H + \frac{e^2}{R} + \frac{e^2}{\rho} \left\{ \frac{\left(1 + \frac{\rho}{R}\right) e^{-\frac{2R}{\rho}} - \left(\frac{R}{\rho} + 1\right) e^{-\frac{R}{\rho}} - \frac{\rho}{R}}{1 + \left(1 + \frac{R}{\rho} + \frac{R^2}{3\rho^2}\right) e^{-\frac{R}{\rho}}} \right\}. \quad \text{(VII.13)}$$

When R is infinitely large $\bar{E} = -E_H$. If the function in VII.13 is
plotted against R, a curve of the correct form is obtained, the
minimum occurring at $1 \cdot 32$ Å, at which separation the energy is
$-15 \cdot 355$ electron volts. Since $-E_H = -13 \cdot 595$ eV, the dissociation
energy is calculated to be $1 \cdot 76$ eV. Therefore the error in the dissociation energy is about 37%.

In order to improve this result a modification that can easily be
made to the trial function is one that was used in the helium calculations. That is, the scale of the $1s$ wave functions is altered and
the following function is employed:

$$\psi = e^{-z' \frac{r_A}{\rho}} + e^{-z' \frac{r_B}{\rho}}. \quad \text{(VII.14)}$$

It is found that the minimum value of the energy is obtained at $R = 1·06$ Å, the experimental value, with $Z' = 1·228$, and the calculated dissociation energy is 2·25 eV. The error is reduced to 19%. (Finkelstein and Horowitz (1928).)

The combined effect of the two nuclei would be expected to increase the probability of the electrons being in the region between them. In order to give effect to this Dickinson (1933) employed:

$$(1s_A{}^{Z'} + C.2p_A{}^{Z''}) + (1s_B{}^{Z'} + C.2p_B{}^{Z''}), \qquad (VII.15)$$

where the $2p$ orbitals were those concentrated along the line joining the nuclei. The effect of adding some of the $2p$ type orbital is therefore to *polarise* the $1s$ orbital. The sign was chosen so that the magnitude of the two orbitals in the internuclear region was increased. The $1s$ and $2p$ functions were assigned separate effective nuclear charges. The energy was minimised for $R = 1·06$ Å, with $Z' = 1·247, Z'' = 2·868$ and $C = 0·145$. The dissociation energy was calculated to be 2·652 eV (error 5%).

Gurney and Magee (1950), when treating the hydrogen molecule, suggested that a very simple way of increasing the electron probability in the internuclear region would be to continue to use simple $1s$ type orbitals but to displace their centres a little from each nuclei towards the other. Hurley (1954) applied this method to $H_2{}^+$ and obtained a dissociation energy of 2·66 eV by displacing the two $1s$ orbitals (having $Z' = 1·23$) 0·061 Å along the nuclear axis. The calculated internuclear distance was 1·05 Å. This is very good, since this function involves only two adjustable parameters as against Dickinson's three. One difficulty associated with this type of function is that the integrals are more difficult to evaluate and this is likely to prevent its extension to molecules other than $H_2{}^+$ and H_2.

Guillemin and Zener (1929) also employed a function which serves to polarise each of the component atomic orbitals, and increase the electron density between the nuclei. This was

$$e^{-Z'\frac{r_A}{\rho}}.e^{-Z''\frac{r_B}{\rho}} + e^{-Z'\frac{r_B}{\rho}}.e^{-Z''\frac{r_A}{\rho}}. \qquad (VII.16)$$

The best values of Z' and Z'' were 1·13 and 0·23. This gave a dissociation energy of 2·78 eV and an equilibrium internuclear distance of 1·06. It therefore seems that multiplication by the polarising factor $e^{-0·23\frac{r_B}{\rho}}$ achieves a more accurate polarisation of the $1s_A{}^{Z'}$ orbital than does the Dickinson method.

James (1935) found that with

$$= e^{-Z'(r_A+r_B)/R}\left\{1 + C\left(\frac{r_A - r_B}{R}\right)^2\right\} \qquad \text{(VII.17)}$$

the calculated dissociation energy is 2·772 eV, which is extremely good for a function involving only two adjustable parameters (Z and C). The new form of the exponential term 'concentrates' the electron in the internuclear region. However, apparently it overdoes this, and the term in $\left(\dfrac{r_A - r_B}{R}\right)^2$ serves to reduce this excessive concentration. It would seem that a successful function is obtained more by accident than design.

The above functions have been considered in some detail, because they illustrate the ways in which workers have tried to obtain functions of a reasonably successful kind, which are fairly simple. For example, none of the functions involved more than three adjustable parameters, and it is conceivable that such functions, or ones like them, might be used in more complex problems. In fact, it is possible to be even more accurate than any of the above, because it has been possible to achieve a separation of the wave equation of $H_2{}^+$ and Burrau (1927) carried out a very accurate treatment by numerical integration. Other very accurate treatments have been made by Hylleraas (1931) and Jaffe (1934), but none of these could conceivably be transferred to any other system.

Bates, Ledsham and Stewart (1953) have carried out very accurate treatments of the ground state, and several of the excited states of $H_2{}^+$.

VII.3 Binding in the Hydrogen Molecule Ion

Before examining what factors contribute to binding in the hydrogen molecule ion, it is necessary to introduce the Virial Theorem, as applied to systems in which the potential energy is only electrostatic, and therefore consists of a number of terms which are inversely proportional to the separation between charges. All atomic and molecular systems are of this kind, if magnetic interactions are neglected. The Virial Theorem states that, for an equilibrium condition of such a system,

$$E = -\bar{T} = \frac{\bar{V}}{2},$$ (VII.18)

where $\bar{V}$ is the average potential energy, and $\bar{T}$ the average kinetic energy. Therefore, for the equilibrium configuration of a stable molecule, the average potential energy must be lower and the average kinetic energy higher than for the dissociated system. This follows because, on forming the molecule, E decreases (i.e. ΔE is negative).

For the most simple function of the preceding section (VII.1) Hirschfelder and Kincaid (1937) showed that, for the equilibrium internuclear distance, $E = -15\cdot30$ eV, $\bar{T} = +10\cdot37$ eV and $\bar{V} = -25\cdot67$ eV. This result is in serious disagreement with the Virial Theorem. For the separated systems $E = -13\cdot595$, $\bar{T} = +13\cdot595$ and $\bar{V} = -27\cdot190$ eV, which means that the calculated lowering in E is achieved by a lowering in the kinetic energy, there being actually an increase in the potential energy. This is entirely different from what must be obtained in the real hydrogen molecule ion. It would be very unwise therefore to reach any conclusion from this function as to why there is binding in H_2^+. It gives such a totally wrong account of how that energy is made up.

It can be shown that the introduction of a scale factor into the wave function (e.g. the Z' in VII.14) automatically results in the Virial Theorem being satisfied. Therefore, all the remaining functions of the last section will obey the Virial Theorem.

If a calculation is made of the interaction of a hydrogen atom (A) with a proton (i.e. if the trial function is just $1s_A$), it is found that the maximum lowering of the energy is very small, and that such a function gives no account of the fact that H_2^+ involves quite a strong bond. Because a dissociation energy comparable to the true value is obtained with the function $1s_A + 1s_B$, it is often said that the binding arises from an exchange force, or alternatively that binding results from a resonance between the structures $H + H^+$ (first term in VII.1 and in VII.14) and $H^+ + H$ (second term in VII.1 and in VII.14). Added weight is given to this by the importance of integrals such as the second term in VII.11 in leading to a lowering of the energy.

Because the results obtained from VII.1 do not satisfy the Virial Theorem this function will not be discussed further. The function VII.14 is similar to VII.1 but satisfies the Virial Theorem. The component functions, which are $1s$ in type, have been drawn more closely to the nuclei ($Z' > 1$) than the simple $1s$ functions. The region in which both the component functions have a considerable value is the region between the nuclei. So it is here that the square of the wave function, the probability, is particularly enhanced at the expense of other regions. Moreover the effect of Z being greater than unity is that the orbitals on the 'outside' of each atom are not so extensive; also in this region the effect of the orbital centred on the other atom is not great. Therefore the function involves a transfer of electron density to the internuclear region. It is this transfer that is the important factor in lowering the potential energy which the Virial Theorem requires to be the important factor providing binding. Further, all the other functions achieve increasingly good results in the calculation of the dissociation energy by increasing still further the probability of the electron being in the internuclear region. This transfer is limited because the orbital must not be too localised as this would lead to an undue increase in the kinetic energy. However, plotting the wave functions shows that, *within these limits*, they become increasingly satisfactory as they increase the probability in this inter-bond region.

It is more realistic to regard the protons as being held together in H_2^+ by an increase in the electron probability in the region between them than to say that it is due to *electron exchange* or to *resonance* between the structures $H + H^+$ and $H^+ + H$, for neither of these statements adds appreciably to our understanding of the phenomenon.

VII.4 The Hydrogen Molecule

The hydrogen molecule has a dissociation energy (D_e) of 4·75 eV and an equilibrium internuclear distance (r_e) of 0·7417 Å. The total energy of the equilibrium configuration is therefore 31·94 eV less than when the protons and electrons are infinitely separated.

For the ground state of the helium atom, the first trial function was obtained by putting both electrons in the lowest orbital of He^+, each being there independently of the other. This is an obvious starting point for this treatment of the hydrogen molecule but, having regard to the discussion in Section VII.2 of H_2^+, the question arises as to what should be used for the basic one-electron function. The situation in H_2 is different from that in He. For the latter the accurate wave functions of He^+ were available in a simple analytical form. This is not so for the wave functions of H_2^+. Here is the first difficulty in the treatment of polyelectronic molecules; the exact basic one-electron wave functions are not available.

Calculations for the two-electron systems H_2 which are based on the product of *separate* one-electron wave functions are described as *molecular orbital* calculations. The wave functions for the $1s, 2s, 2p$ etc. of atoms are described as atomic orbitals because they refer to atomic systems. The orbitals VII.1, VII.14, VII.15, VII.16 and VII.17 are described as molecular orbitals since they are the corresponding functions for a molecular system. If the electrons of a polyelectronic system occupy separate independent orbitals the description is called a molecular orbital one. That is, for the ground state of hydrogen, the function

$$\psi(1, 2) = \phi_a(1) \cdot \phi_a(2) \tag{VII.19}$$

is a molecular orbital one, the total function being made up of one part dependent on the coordinates of electron 1 only, and a second part dependent on the coordinates of 2 only. For excited states of two-electron systems, the molecular orbital function consists of two separate parts

$$\psi(1, 2) = \frac{1}{\sqrt{2}}\phi_a(1) \cdot \phi_b(2) \pm \frac{1}{\sqrt{2}}\phi_a(2) \cdot \phi_b(1), \tag{VII.20}$$

since the Pauli Principle must be satisfied.

Our examination of H_2^+ showed that there are many ways that can be used for approximating to true molecular orbitals. However, for complex systems, the type that has been most used because of its simplicity, and despite its inaccuracy, is that exemplified by VII.1. Because the molecular orbital is written as the sum of separate atomic orbitals, it is said to be formed by a linear combination of atomic orbitals (LCAO). In the remainder of this book we shall encounter many molecular orbitals of this type (LCAO MOs).

Returning to the specific case of H_2 the simplest approach will be examined first. That is, the simplest trial function of H_2^+ will be selected (VII.1). Using this the trial wave function (not normalised) for H_2 is

$$\psi(1, 2) = [1s_A(1) + 1s_B(1)][1s_A(2) + 1s_B(2)], \qquad \text{(VII.21)}$$

the electrons being labelled 1 and 2 and $1s_A(1)$ representing $N \cdot e^{-r_{A1}}$ where r_{A1} is the distance between nucleus A and electron 1.

The Hamiltonian H for H_2 is

$$H = -\frac{h^2}{8\pi^2 m}(\nabla_1{}^2 + \nabla_2{}^2) - \frac{e^2}{r_{A1}} - \frac{e^2}{r_{A2}} - \frac{e^2}{r_{B1}} - \frac{e^2}{r_{B2}} + \frac{e^2}{R} + \frac{e^2}{r_{12}}. \qquad \text{(VII.22)}$$

Using this, the energy corresponding to VII.21 can be calculated in the usual way, though some of the integrals are not easy to evaluate. The dissociation energy is calculated to be 2·681 eV and the equilibrium internuclear distance to be 0·850 Å. This is not very successful, since the calculated dissociation energy is only about 60% of the true value. However, this is not surprising, because we know that VII.1 is not a good function for H_2^+, the error in the dissociation was, even there, 37%. Further, VII.1 and VII.21 are unsatisfactory in that, because they contain no scale factor, they do not satisfy the Virial Theorem, and do not provide a satisfactory balance between mean kinetic and mean potential energies.

Proceeding as for H_2^+, an obvious way of improving VII.19 is to introduce a scale factor, using the function

$$\psi(1, 2) = [1s_A{}^{Z'}(1) + 1s_B{}^{Z'}(1)][1s_A{}^{Z'}(2) + 1s_B{}^{Z'}(2)] \qquad \text{(VII.23)}$$

when $1s_A{}^{Z'}(1) \equiv e^{-Z'\frac{r_{A1}}{\rho}}$. With this function, the energy is minimised for $Z' = 1\cdot197$, the dissociation energy being calculated to be

3·470 eV. As with H_2^+, the advantage of including a variable parameter Z' is considerable, but the dissociation energy is only 73% of
the true value.

The success and simplicity of the James function for H_2^+ (VII.17)
suggests that a molecular orbital treatment of H_2 based on it might
be accurate. In fact the dissociation energy (3·4 eV), calculated by
Rahman (1957), is less than that obtained using VII.23 which involves only one adjustable parameter. Coulson (1938) developed
this approach still further rather in the manner that Hylleraas had
used for helium. He made calculations only for R equal to the
experimental r_e, and with the function

$$e^{-Z \cdot \frac{r_A + r_B}{\rho}} \left\{ 1 + a \left[\frac{r_A - r_B}{R} \right]^2 + b \left[\frac{r_A + r_B}{R} \right] \right. $$
$$\left. + c \left[\frac{r_A + r_B}{R} \right]^2 + d \left[\frac{r_A + r_B}{R} \right] \left[\frac{r_A - r_B}{R} \right]^2 \right\}, \quad \text{(VII.24)}$$

he obtained a lowering of the energy relative to 2H of 3.603 eV.
He came to the conclusion that the best dissociation energy that
could be obtained by a molecular orbital approach without configuration interaction (i.e. with a function of the type VII.19) would
be about 3·63 eV. This is only 76% of the true dissociation energy.
Moreover, it appears that little is to be gained by using a complex
function such as VII.24 when the much simpler VII.23 is almost as
satisfactory.

The fault of a molecular orbital treatment, even the best, is the
same as that of the $1s^2$ treatment of the ground state of helium; in
neither function is there any term which serves to reduce the probability of the electrons coming close to one another. In both treatments, the electrons have probability distributions which are
independent of one another. This is clearly unsatisfactory.

This inability to allow, at all completely, for the charge correlation energy by any molecular orbital treatment, renders even the
best of them unsatisfactory for obtaining a worth-while value of
the dissociation energy. It is therefore necessary to examine how
electron correlation might be introduced into the wave function,
preferably by some means that does not result in a great increase
in the labour of evaluating integrals.

If the multiplication in VII.21 is carried out the following equation is obtained:

$$\psi(1, 2) = [1s_A(1) . 1s_A(2) + 1s_B(2) . 1s_B(1)]$$
$$+ [1s_A(1) . 1s_A(2) + 1s_B(1) . 1s_B(2)]. \qquad (VII.25)$$

The second pair of terms are particularly large when the electrons are close together, the first when both electrons are near nucleus A and the second when both are near nucleus B. Therefore, if this pair of terms were omitted, there would have been some reduction in the probability of some of the configurations involving electrons being close to one another, which were given a particularly high probability by the simple MO function. Moreover, this does not reduce to any great extent the probability of finding both electrons in the region between the nuclei.

The trial function

$$\psi(1, 2) = 1s_A(1) . 1s_B(2) + 1s_A(2) . 1s_B(1) \qquad (VII.26)$$

was first used by Heitler and London (1927), though as a result of a different argument which was the following one. If the two hydrogen atoms are infinitely separated, function VII.26 becomes one of the exact solutions of the system (the other is VII.26 with a negative sign which, for $R = \infty$, is degenerate with VII.26). If therefore the additional forces that come into operation when the two hydrogen atoms are brought together are treated as the perturbation, VII.26 may be regarded as the simple unperturbed function for the hydrogen molecule.

By applying the methods of Chapter V to VII.26, the mean energy is obtained as

$$E = \frac{J + K}{1 + S^2}, \qquad (VII.27)$$

where $J = \iint 1s_A(1) . 1s_B(2) . H . 1s_A(1) . 1s_B(2) \, d\tau_1 \, d\tau_2, \qquad (VII.28)$

and $K = \iint 1s_A(1) . 1s_B(2) . H . 1s_A(2) . 1s_B(1) \, d\tau_1 \, d\tau_2, \qquad (VII.29)$

and S is given by VII.9. For function $1s_A(1) . 1s_B(2)$, the energy would have been given by J alone. This leads to a potential energy curve having a very shallow minimum, r_e being $1 \cdot 0$ Å and the dissociation energy 0·4 eV. The dissociation energy calculated using VII.27 (i.e. function VII.26) is, however, 3·14 eV, the bond length being 0·869 Å.

By analogy with the molecular orbital treatment of H_2 and treatments of He and H_2^+, an obvious way of improving VII.26 is to introduce a scale factor Z' into the exponential. This was done by Wang (1928) who found that the calculated dissociation energy is 3·76 eV, the bond length being 0·76 Å and for this the value of Z' is 1·166. This is rather less than the values of Z' which were needed to obtain the best dissociation energies for H_2^+ and H_2 using the molecular orbital method.

This trial function has therefore been extremely successful, because, with only one adjustable parameter (Z'), it has been possible to obtain a dissociation energy better than that obtainable by the best molecular orbital treatment. This shows the importance of allowing for electron correlation.

Many attempts have been made to improve the Heitler–London–Wang function. These are of three types and some workers have attempted to include all three types of improvement. These may be summarised as follows: (I) Modifications which increase the probability of finding the electrons in the inter-bond region (Rosen (1931), and Gurney and Magee (1950)); (II) Modifications which confer greater freedom of independent movement on the electrons; that is, decrease electron correlation (Weinbaum (1933)); (III) Modifications which add additional electron correlation effects (Hirschfelder and Linnett (1950), and Lennard-Jones and Pople (1951)).

Rosen modified the Heitler–London function by replacing $1s_A \left(e^{-\frac{r_A}{\rho}}\right)$ by

$$e^{-\frac{r_A}{\rho}}\left(1 + a.\frac{r_A}{\rho}\cos\theta_A\right) \qquad (VII.30)$$

where θ is measured from the axis AB. The function $1s_B$ was similarly modified. This is very similar to the modification made by Dickinson in H_2^+. When Rosen made the substitution VII.30 and also included a scale factor, he obtained a dissociation energy of 4·02 eV (85% of the true value). Gurney and Magee allowed for the polarisation of the atomic orbitals, in the manner described in Section VII.2, by retaining $1s$ type orbitals but moving their centres towards the other nucleus. When a scale factor was used Gurney and Magee obtained a dissociation energy of $4 \cdot 16$ eV (88% of the true value). This is the best energy that has been obtained using a two-constant function, and it is a good example of how the development of a successful wave function demands insight into the electronic situation, and ingenuity in constructing a function in as simple a form as possible to meet the situation.

The Heitler–London function, VII.26, was obtained by dropping two terms from the molecular orbital function, VII.21. It was explained that this would allow for electron correlation. Weinbaum suggested that leaving these two terms out altogether might be too drastic and so he made use of the trial function:

$$\psi(1, 2) = [1s_A(1) \cdot 1s_B(2) + 1s_A(2) \cdot 1s_B(1)] \\ + C[1s_A(1) \cdot 1s_A(2) + 1s_B(1) \cdot 1s_B(2)]. \quad \text{(VII.31)}$$

This is equivalent to reducing the electron correlation relative to the Heitler–London function. With VII.31 and using a scale factor Weinbaum obtained a dissociation energy of $4 \cdot 00$ eV ($Z' = 1.193$ and $C = 0 \cdot 256$). The energy is considerably improved relative to that obtained using the Heitler–London function, implying the latter does include too much correlation.

The method of Heitler and London has been described as the valence bond method, and their function as that of an electron pair bond. In this terminology, the Weinbaum function can be described as involving *resonance* between the three structures H—H, H^-H^+ and H^+H^-. It is therefore a combination of the valence bond method with the concept of resonance.

Weinbaum also combined the polarisation modification of Rosen with function VII.31 and obtained a dissociation energy of $4 \cdot 10$ eV.

The functions mentioned so far have only included axial correlation. That is, they have not included any terms which favour the electrons being on opposite sides of a plane which contains the nuclei. This may be called azimuthal correlation and is a function of ϕ, the angle round the internuclear axis. Hirschfelder and Linnett included this form of correlation by a method based on that used

H

102 *Wave Mechanics and Valency*

by Rosen and Dickinson. They added to the wave functions terms involving the $2p$ atomic orbitals with their axes at right angles to the internuclear axis, whereas Rosen had added a term equivalent to a $2p$ orbital with its axis along the line AB. Including this, together with Rosen's and Weinbaum's modifications and a scale factor, Hirschfelder and Linnett obtained a dissociation energy of 4·25 eV. However, their function was rather complex since it involved four adjustable constants. Lennard-Jones and Pople also introduced azimuthal correlation together with ionic terms, and obtained a dissociation energy of 4·10 eV.

All the attempts to introduce electron correlation described so far have avoided the direct inclusion of terms involving r_{12}. The reason for this is that the inclusion of such terms introduces integrals into the expression for the energy which are difficult to solve. However, James and Coolidge (1933) attacked the problem of the hydrogen molecule in much the same way that Hylleraas attacked the ground state of the helium atom. They used a function of the type

$$e^{-z\frac{r_{A1}+r_{B1}}{\rho}} \cdot e^{-z\frac{r_{A2}+r_{B2}}{\rho}} \left\{ 1 + \Sigma\, C_{hjklm}\left(\frac{r_{A1}+r_{B1}}{R}\right)^h \right.$$
$$\left. \left(\frac{r_{A2}+r_{B2}}{R}\right)^j \left(\frac{r_{A1}-r_{B1}}{R}\right)^k \left(\frac{r_{A2}-r_{B2}}{R}\right)^l \left(\frac{r_{12}}{R}\right)^m \right\}. \quad (VII.32)$$

There are certain restrictions on the terms in the polynomial. For instance, k and l must be even, and also there must be symmetry between the terms of electron 1 and electron 2 that are included. James and Coolidge made calculations for a four-term polynomial, a ten-term one and a twelve-term, all of which contained a term or terms in r_{12}. In each case the coefficients C_{hjklm} were chosen so that the energy was minimised. Dissociation energies of 4·53, 4·70 and 4·72 eV were obtained. This is the most successful treatment that has been carried out for the hydrogen molecule. It is significant that, although these calculations were published 26 years ago, it is only very recently (Kolos and Roothaan (1960)) that there has been any extension at all of this method, a function containing about 50 terms having been employed. Using this the calculated dissociation energy is probably even more reliable than the experimental value.

However, it does not seem that the successful treatment of more complex molecules will be in a development based on the Coolidge–James approach, but that attempts must be made with more simple functions of the valence bond or molecular orbital type; or alternatively some completely new ways of constructing a trial wave function must be devised. These calculations of James and Coolidge like those of Hylleraas constituted a great *tour de force* but unfortunately both have proved sterile as regards their development for more complex systems.

Frost and Braunstein (1951) have also made use of a function involving r_{12}. This function

$$\psi(1, 2) = [1s_A{}^{Z'}(1) + 1s_B{}^{Z'}(1)][1s_A{}^{Z'}(2) + 1s_B{}^{Z'}(2)]$$
$$[1 + ar_{12}] \quad \text{(VII.33)}$$

may be described as a molecular orbital function with correlation. Using this they obtained a dissociation energy of $4 \cdot 11 \, \text{eV} \, (Z' = 1 \cdot 285)$. This is the best energy obtained using a two-parameter function except for that due to Gurney and Magee.

Before concluding this discussion of the treatments of the hydrogen molecule, molecular orbital treatments based on configuration interaction will be described. This may be compared with the Taylor and Parr treatment of the helium atom.

The lowest molecular orbital of $H_2{}^+$ on the LCAO approximation is VII.1, $(1s_A + 1s_B)$. The next excited state is the combination that is degenerate with it at $R = \infty$, namely $(1s_A - 1s_B)$. Therefore the most simple function for H_2 which involves configuration interaction is

$$\psi = [1s_A(1) + 1s_B(1)][1s_A(2) + 1s_B(2)]$$
$$+ \lambda[1s_A(1) - 1s_B(1)][1s_A(2) - 1s_B(2)]. \quad \text{(VII.34)}$$

Terms in which one electron is in the lowest state and the other in the first excited one, cannot be included as they would destroy the symmetry of the wave function, which must be maintained. If VII.34 is multiplied out, it is found to be identical with the Weinbaum function VII.31, the coefficient c being equal to $\dfrac{1 - \lambda}{1 + \lambda}$. Since the dissociation energy obtained using the Weinbaum function with a scale factor is 4·00 eV this is considerable improvement on the 3·47 eV obtained with $\lambda = 0$.

The fact that VII.34 is identical with VII.31 illustrates an important point. The function VII.31 is as complete a function as it is possible to construct on the basis of a valence bond treatment with resonance with other structures, providing that one limits one's choice to terms based on $1s$ functions only. Likewise VII.34 is the most complete LCAO molecular orbital treatment with configuration interaction, with the limitation that molecular orbitals constructed only from $1s$ orbitals are used. Therefore the complete valence-bond/resonance function is identical with the complete LCAO molecular orbital/configuration interaction function. This is true for all systems. Therefore any judgment between the two treatments must be based on the relative success that is obtained with incomplete treatments of the two kinds.

Rahman (1957) has also made calculations which are based on a molecular orbital procedure with configuration interaction, but the molecular orbitals employed as the basis were of a type which had been found particularly effective for H_2^+. Functions of this James-type were used and, as stated earlier, with just one configuration, the dissociation energy was calculated to be 3·4 eV. With the inclusion of two other terms to improve the form of the $1s^2$ function, and with three other terms representing excited configurations, the calculated dissociation energy was increased to 4·34 eV. This is a fairly successful value though it must be remembered that the function contains seven adjustable constants, so that it does not seem that this is as profitable an approach as might have been expected, though it does have the advantage of containing no r_{12} terms.

One of the most significant factors in modern wave mechanics is the advent of the high-speed computer. As a result of this variation functions have been proposed which are particularly well suited for handling by high-speed computers. An example of this for H_2 is to be found in the work of Harris (1957), whose functions are somewhat reminiscent of that proposed by Guillemin and Zener for H_2^+, though greater flexibility is introduced by including additional terms. Using just one configuration (four potentially adjustable constants) Harris obtained 4·16 eV for the dissociation energy. With a more complicated two-configuration function involving more adjustable constants, he obtained $D_e = 4.44$ eV. This appears to be promising, but the dissociation energy is still about 6% less than the true value.

The above account of the trial wave functions that have been used for hydrogen is not an exhaustive one. The primary aim has been to describe the types of functions that have been tested and to comment briefly on the probable reasons for choosing them and the possible causes of their success or failure.

VII.5 Binding in the Hydrogen Molecule

Because of the success of the Heitler–London function and the importance of the term K in the expression (VII.27) obtained for the energy, it is often said that binding in the hydrogen molecule is due to exchange. This implies that valency forces arise from the exchange of the electrons between the two atoms, and that binding energy is to be described as an exchange energy.

It seems to the author that such views are dangerous for they imply to the uninitiated that there is some new form of energy. This is not the case. The electronic energy of atoms and molecules can be described in terms of potential energy and kinetic energy in virtually the same way as if the system were classical.* Therefore it would seem to be better to consider how the potential and kinetic energy changes, rather than to invent new terms such as exchange energy.

The term *exchange energy* was encountered in the application of the Perturbation and Variation Methods to two-particle systems in Chapters V and VI. There it took account of the fact that, because of the Pauli Principle, there is a correlation between the mutual positions of the two electrons which is dependent on whether their spins are parallel or opposed. Because electrons carry a charge this

---

* There are some differences. For example, in wave mechanics, configurations in which the potential energy exceeds the total energy and the wave mechanical kinetic energy, as defined by a formula like I.5, is negative are allowed. However, the probability of such configurations is usually small and valency is not related in any important way to such differences from classical behaviour.

leads to an effect on the energy. For this reason the term *spin correlation energy* was adopted as being more informative than the term *exchange energy*, which was discarded.

However, the *exchange energy* that has been encountered in this chapter (VII.27 and VII.29) is not related to the same effect. In the He atom the basic functions were the *true* solutions for the one-electron problem He^+ and therefore had a well-defined significance. As a consequence the *spin correlation energy* had a well-defined significance. In this problem, the basic one-electron functions of H_2^+ are not used to construct the wave function of H_2. The exchange term VII.29 arises because of the approximation used, and its particular form follows from the nature of the approximate function used. If the treatment had been similar to that of helium, and the true one-electron function of H_2^+ had been used as a basis, no exchange term would have appeared. As for the ground state of helium, the only term would have been a coulomb term because when two electrons are in the same orbital there is no spin correlation effect (i.e. no exchange). The term *exchange energy* was applied because of the form of the integral. That is, the term was introduced for a mathematical rather than a physically significant reason.

The function VII.26 is unsatisfactory for the same reason as VII.1; that is, because the Virial Theorem is not satisfied. As a result, though there is a lowering of the energy, the pattern of the change in the kinetic and potential energies is entirely wrong. Therefore any conclusions about the cause of binding which are derived from VII.26 are bound to be extremely suspect. All the other functions achieve a marked lowering in the potential energy, which, by the Virial Theorem, is essential for chemical bonding, by the increase of electron probability in the internuclear region. The arguments regarding this are essentially the same as were used in Section VII.3 for H_2^+, and are true even for such simple functions as VII.23 and for the Heitler–London function VII.26. It has already been pointed out that the omission of the ionic terms from the MO function did not reduce, to any great extent, the probability of finding both electrons in the region between the nuclei. What this omission did was to reduce the probability of finding the two electrons simultaneously near the same nucleus.

Therefore it would appear that, as for H_2^+, binding results from the increase of negative charge between the two positively charged nuclei.

Because of the nature of wave mechanics, and of the Virial Theorem, changes in kinetic energy cannot be ignored. However, this does not alter the fact that binding can only be achieved if the mean potential energy in the molecular system is lower than the mean potential energy in the two separated atomic systems.

VII.6 The Excited States of H_2^+ and H_2

The simplest approximate expression for the lowest orbital of H_2^+ is VII.1, which if normalised is

$$\psi = \frac{1}{\sqrt{2(1 + S_{1s})}} (1s_A + 1s_B) \qquad \text{(VII.35)}$$

where S_{1s} is the same as S in VII.9. At infinite separation the degenerate orbitals $1s_A$ and $1s_B$ can be combined as in VII.35, the other member of the pair which is orthogonal to it being

$$\psi = \frac{1}{\sqrt{2(1 - S_{1s})}} (1s_A - 1s_B) \qquad \text{(VII.36)}$$

(cf. Section III). When the nuclei are brought together the energy associated with VII.35, as we have seen, decreases. The energy associated with VII.36 must be greater than that associated with VII.35, because there is a central planar nodal surface across the internuclear axis whereas VII.35 has no node. Experience has shown that increasing the number of nodes leads to an increase in energy. In fact the energy of VII.36 increases continuously as the nuclei are brought together. From the form of the orbital (the planar nodal surface), it would clearly become more and more like the $2p_z$ orbital of He^+ (z being the internuclear axis), as the nuclei are brought closer and closer. The electronic energy of a $2p$ orbital of He^+ is equal to that of a $1s$ orbital of H, so that there is no lowering of electronic energy to compensate internuclear repulsion. The orbital VII.35 becomes more and more like the $1s$ orbital of helium as the nuclei approach one another. The electronic energy of the $1s$ orbital in He^+ is $-4E_H$, where $-E_H$ is the electronic energy of the $1s$ orbital of H. So in this case there is a lowering of electronic energy which at values of R greater than about 0·4 Å outweighs nuclear repulsion. The orbital VII.35 is therefore a *bonding* orbital while VII.36 is an *antibonding* one.

As two hydrogen nuclei with a single electron between them are brought together all the states of separated systems must pass through states of the molecule to states of the so-called *united atom*, this being the atomic system to which the molecule approaches as the nuclei are brought very close together. To a first approximation, therefore, the wave functions of the other excited states of $H_2{}^+$ may be constructed by the same procedure that has just been used (VII.35 and VII.36). The result, for the orbitals of the hydrogen atom which have a principal quantum of 2, is as follows:

$$\frac{1}{\sqrt{2(1 + S_{2s})}}(2s_A + 2s_B) \quad \longrightarrow \quad 2s \text{ in } He^+, \qquad \text{(VII.37)}$$

$$\frac{1}{\sqrt{2(1 - S_{2s})}}(2s_A - 2s_B) \quad \longrightarrow \quad 3p_z \text{ in } He^+, \qquad \text{(VII.38)}$$

$$\frac{1}{\sqrt{2(1 + S_{2p_z})}}(2p_z + 2p_z) \quad \longrightarrow \quad 3s \text{ in } He^+, \qquad \text{(VII.39)}$$

$$\frac{1}{\sqrt{2(1 - S_{2p_z})}}(2p_z - 2p_z) \quad \longrightarrow \quad 4p_z \text{ in } He^+, \qquad \text{(VII.40)}$$

$$\frac{1}{\sqrt{2(1 + S_{2p_x})}}(2p_x + 2p_x) \quad \longrightarrow \quad 2p_x \text{ in } He^+, \qquad \text{(VII.41)}$$

$$\frac{1}{\sqrt{2(1 - S_{2p_x})}}(2p_x - 2p_x) \quad \longrightarrow \quad 3d_{xz} \text{ in } He^+, \qquad \text{(VII.42)}^*$$

and similarly for the pair involving $2p_y$, which must be degenerate at all separations with the pair involving $2p_x$. In the above, the real forms of the $2p$ functions have been used, the imaginary forms $2p_{+1}$ and $2p_{-1}$ might have been used in place of $2p_x$ and $2p_y$. The orbitals VII.37–VII.42 are shown diagrammatically in Figure 11.

---

* In VII.39 to VII.42 the subscripts A and B on $2p_z$, etc., have been omitted. The reader is to presume that, within each bracket, one $2p$ orbital is on atom A and the other on B.

The relations VII.37–VII.40 are, in fact, somewhat idealised for VII.37 and VII.39 (and VII.38 and 40 are a similar pair) have the same symmetry with respect to the line joining the two atoms and

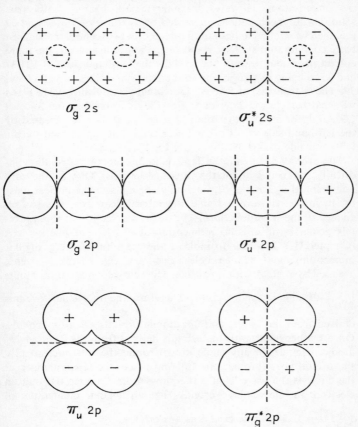

Fig. 11. Diagrammatic representation of the molecular orbitals of H_2 *which are derived from the 2s and 2p orbitals of the hydrogen atoms. Nodes are shown by broken lines*

the central point on that line which is a centre of symmetry. Consequently the functions on the left of VII.37 and 39 are true for the widely separated atoms and the functions on the right are true for the 'united atom'. However, for intermediate separations the true solutions are much better represented by mixtures of VII.37 and 39 (i.e. there is strong configuration interaction between these idealised basic configurations). As a result of the above argument, the more correct presentation would be to show the left-hand sides of VII.37 and 39 as being related jointly to the right-hand sides of VII.37 and 39. The reason that the above individual relationships were listed was that for He the $2s$ level of He^+ (37) is lower than the $3s$ level (39), and, for atoms other than hydrogen, the state represented by the left-hand side of VII.37 is lower than that represented by the left-hand side of VII.39. (Similarly for VII.38 and 40.)

The orbitals involving the $1s$, $2s$ and $2p_z$ functions are all cylindrically symmetric about the internuclear axis. That is, they are not changed by rotation through any angle about the nuclear axis; or, in any circle drawn round the internuclear axis, there is no change in the wave functions. Therefore, an electron in these orbitals possesses no angular momentum about the internuclear axis (Chapter III). In order to indicate the magnitude of the angular momentum about the internuclear axis the Greek letters σ, π, δ, etc., are used by analogy with s, p, d, etc. They correspond to 0, 1, 2 units $\left(\dfrac{h}{2\pi}\right)$ of angular momentum. Therefore the molecular orbitals derived from the $1s$, $2s$, and $2p_z$ atomic orbitals are all σ-orbitals. On the other hand, with the orbitals derived from the $2p_x$ and $2p_y$ atomic orbitals, in any circle drawn round the internuclear axis, the orbital goes through one full wave – i.e. the circumference of the circle is the wave length. It follows from Chapter III, that an electron, in one of these orbitals, has an angular momentum of $1\dfrac{h}{2\pi}$. It is therefore described as a π-orbital.

In addition the nuclear system of the molecule H_2^+ has a centre of symmetry. Therefore the value of ψ^2, the probability, must be the same at two positions such that the line joining them is bisected by the centre of symmetry. It is said that ψ^2 must remain unchanged on inverting through the centre. There are then two possibilities for ψ: either it remains unchanged, when the wave function is said to be symmetric with respect to inversion in the centre (represented by a subscript g); or it changes in sign, when it is said to be antisymmetric (subscript u).

These qualities enable us to describe the molecular orbitals more compactly. The orbital VII.35 is described as $\sigma_g 1s$, VII.36 as $\sigma_u * 1s$, the asterisk denoting that it is one with higher energy. Those that are derived from the atomic orbitals of quantum number 2 are $\sigma_g 2s$, $\sigma_u * 2s$, $\sigma_g 2p$, $\sigma_u * 2p$, $\pi_u 2p$ and $\pi_g * 2p$, the last two being doubly degenerate (cf. Chapter III).

For the hydrogen molecule, the description of excited states can now be achieved in the same way as for the helium atom. For example, if one electron is in the $\sigma_g 1s$ orbital and the other in the $\sigma_g 2s$ orbital there is a singlet state having the wave function

$$\psi = \frac{1}{\sqrt{2}}[\sigma_g 1s(1) . \sigma_g 2s(2) + \sigma_g 1s(2) . \sigma_g 2s(1)], \quad \text{(VII.43)}$$

and a triplet state having

$$\psi = \frac{1}{\sqrt{2}}[\sigma_g 1s(1) . \sigma_g 2s(2) - \sigma_g 1s(2) . \sigma_g 2s(1)]. \quad \text{(VII.44)}$$

Having regard to the connection between the orbitals of the separated species $H + H^+$ and the united 'atom' He^+, and knowing the energies of these, we would expect the orbitals to be in approximately the following order of energy:

$$\sigma_g 1s < \sigma_u * 1s < \sigma_g 2s \sim \pi_u 2p < \sigma_u * 2s \sim \sigma_g 2p \sim \pi_g * 2p < \sigma_g * 2p.$$

It is presumed that the third and fourth in the above list will have approximately the same energy because they pass from levels of principle quantum 2 in $H + H^+$ to the levels of the same principal quantum number in He^+. The next three are grouped together because they pass from principal quantum number 2 in $H + H^+$ to 3 in He^+. The last goes to 4 in He^+.

From the spectrum of H_2 the energies of various states can be obtained. For those states for which one electron is in the $\sigma_g 1s$

orbital and the other in another orbital, it is found that the results confirm the above list surprisingly well. For triplet states the figures are $\sigma_g 1s^2$, 0; $\sigma_g 1s . \sigma_u*1s$, 60,000–90,000 cm^{-1} (the repulsive state, the upper limit of 90,000, is given on the basis of the position of the corresponding singlet state), $\sigma_g 1s . \sigma_g 2s$, 100,063 cm^{-1}, $\sigma_g 1s . \pi_u 2p$ 100,043; $\sigma_g 1s . \sigma_u*2s$, 107,777 cm^{-1}, $\sigma_g 1s . \sigma_g 2p$, 112,770; $\sigma_g 1s . \pi_g*2p$, 112,702 cm^{-1}; $\sigma_g 1s . \sigma_u*2p$, 116,708. The order is just that expected and, in most cases, the equalities to be expected are found. The same type of result would be obtained with the singlet states, but the data are less complete.

The LCAO molecular orbitals just described have been used as the basis of a description of the excited states of $H_2{}^+$ and H_2. There is no doubt that they are very valuable for that purpose, as the data in the last paragraph show. The description gives the correct information about the number and the type of the nodes involved in each orbital. On the other hand, they are of little use for the *a priori* calculation of orbital energies, and therefore of excited states. This has been seen to be true for the ground state. The wave function and calculated energy of the ground state can be improved by configuration interaction. For example, the treatment of Dickinson can be regarded as the employment of configuration interaction, the two states involved being the $\sigma_g 1s$ and the $\sigma_g 2p$. Of course if it is found that the ground state is to be described by

$$\cos \alpha . \sigma_g 1s + \sin \alpha . \sigma_g 2p \qquad \text{(VII.45)}$$

then, in order to maintain orthogonality, the wave function of the excited state must be replaced, to a first approximation by

$$- \sin \alpha . \sigma_g 1s + \cos \alpha . \sigma_g 2p. \qquad \text{(VII.46)}$$

In principle, configuration interaction could be allowed between *all* the approximate wave functions of a given symmetry. If this were done, then an accurate description of all the states of the system of that symmetry would be obtained. However, because the number of wave functions of a given symmetry is infinitely large, this is not a practicable procedure. The question is really: Can reasonable accuracy be obtained with a number of functions that can be handled? The answer is probably 'Yes' for $H_2{}^+$ and 'No' for H_2.

There is another fundamental difficulty about this type of approach to atomic and molecular systems which is often not mentioned. We describe the ground state of helium as $1s^2$, there being two electrons in the $1s$ orbital. However, because of charge correlation the two electrons do not occupy independent orbitals. It is an approximation to describe a system as if they do, and this is so for all states of all atomic and molecular systems containing more than one electron; that is, for virtually everything with which a chemist is concerned. And yet, it is necessary to persist with descriptions of this type for want of anything better. It is true that a description like $1s^2$ does tell us that, in the six-dimensional space $(x_1 y_1 z_1 x_2 y_2 z_2)$ which is necessary to describe the positions of the two particles, there are no nodes. These descriptions always have this limited, but by no means useless, merit. Nevertheless, it must be remembered, when employing descriptions such as $1s2p$ for helium, and $\sigma_g 1s . \pi_u 2p$ for H_2, that the implied independence of the orbitals is illusory, and that the energy is made up of the basic energy of the orbitals together with coulomb energy, spin correlation energy and charge correlation energy (if one chooses to subdivide it in that way) or, at any rate, it is not simply the sum of the two orbital energies. The failure to realise this, constitutes a weakness of some arguments that have been advanced regarding atomic and molecular orbital theory.

VII.7 Conclusion

In this chapter, wave mechanics has been applied, for the first time in this book, to molecular systems. Even though H_2^+ and H_2 only have been considered, the general impression obtained must be that the calculation of such quantities as dissociation energies by wave mechanical means presents enormous problems. It might even be felt that theoretical chemists have shown great temerity in extending their activities to more complex systems, particularly as most of these extensions are based on the simple molecular orbital or valence bond methods that have been described. Admittedly configuration interaction and resonance does allow some improvement to be obtained, particularly as they can now be used more extensively by making use of high-speed computing machines.

However, this view would be unduly gloomy because, in this chapter, it has been shown that wave mechanics can account for the order of magnitude of the strength of a chemical bond. This had not been possible before the application of the Schrödinger equation to the H_2 molecule by Heitler and London. Also, in the last section, the qualitative description of the orbitals of the excited states of H_2^+ was found to be in good agreement with certain spectroscopically observed levels of H_2. Therefore, there is little doubt that wave mechanics can be most powerful in furthering our understanding of chemical phenomena, and for providing a pattern against which to set experimental data. It also proves possible to make use of wave mechanics to inter-relate numerical data of different kinds, this being a particular example of the way in which a pattern is provided. However, it is undoubtedly true that, as yet, the *a priori* calculation of physical quantities is lagging behind the more qualitative and semi-quantitative applications.

CHAPTER VIII

Polyelectronic Atoms and Diatomic Molecules

VIII.1 Introduction

In Chapter IV the orbitals ($1s$, $2s$, $2p$, etc.) of various states of the hydrogen atom were determined. In Chapter VI the occupation of more than one of these in the helium atom was considered. In Sections 2 and 6 of Chapter VII, the one-electron orbitals of the ground and excited states of H_2^+ were described, and in Sections 4 and 6 the occupation of more than two of these in H_2 was discussed. In this chapter systems containing more than two electrons will be examined. Problems that arise are: How is the Pauli Principle satisfied in such systems? What are its consequences? What are the relative energies of the different states in these systems?

VIII.2 The Pauli Principle

The principle requires that, for two configurations (i.e. two sets of electron positions and spin orientations) of a system which differ only in that the two electrons have been interchanged, the value of the wave function shall be the same in magnitude but different in sign. It was shown, in Chapter VI, Section 7, that for two electrons this means that *either* the space function *or* the spin function must change sign. To generalise this, the treatment must be somewhat different. It will now be illustrated for an atomic system.

Suppose that a number of orbitals are defined in which both the space and the spin part are specified (i.e. $1s(n)\alpha(n)$, $1s(n')\beta(n')$, $2p(n'')\alpha(n'')$, etc.). The total wave function must be written as a sum of products, such that terms corresponding to *all* possible permutations of the particles among the orbitals are included in the set. The sign given to each term is then decided in the following way. The sign of one term is fixed; the sign of any other term is then decided by whether that term can be derived from the reference one by an odd or even number of electron interchanges. If the number of interchanges is *even*, the term is given the *same* sign as the reference term; if it is *odd*, it is given the *opposite* sign. This will be illustrated for three electrons in the orbitals, A, B and C, these letters implying the inclusion of both a spin and a space part. The function is

$$A(1)B(2)C(3) - A(1)B(3)C(2) + A(2)B(3)C(1)$$
$$- A(2)B(1)C(3) + A(3)B(1)C(2) - A(3)B(2)C(1). \qquad \text{(VIII.1)}$$

Each term is derived from the previous one by one interchange, and the sign is changed. This is continued until all possible interchanges have been covered. (Function VIII.1 is not normalised.)

This is a general procedure but because with four electrons there are 24 terms; with five, 120 terms; with six, 720 terms and so on, some abbreviated representation is clearly necessary. This can be done by using the determinantal symbolism which summarises what has been said, and which was exemplified in VIII.1. That wave function would be written in the form of a determinant as

$$\begin{vmatrix} A(1) & B(1) & C(1) \\ A(2) & B(2) & C(2) \\ A(3) & B(3) & C(3) \end{vmatrix}. \qquad \text{(VIII.2)}$$

Representation VIII.2 is identical with VIII.1, but it can clearly be extended more compactly to systems containing more electrons.*

If two of the orbitals A and B were the same for both space and spin parts, then VIII.1 and VIII.2 would be zero. This follows from the properties of determinants (Appendix III) and also from VIII.1 in that the terms will occur in cancelling pairs, because interchanging the electrons between the identical orbitals will lead to a new term of the same magnitude, but the reverse sign. Therefore the wave function is zero if two electrons occupy the same orbital (both space and

---

* The reader who is unfamiliar with determinants should realise that a determinant is only a shorthand summary of a particular pattern of terms. There is a rule by which VIII.2 can be transformed to VIII.1. However, other operations can be carried out on determinants more compactly than on the products VIII.1. That is, there is a mathematics of determinants. A few properties of determinants are stated without proof in Appendix III.

spin). Therefore such states do not exist. Two electrons cannot have all their quantum numbers the same.

Suppose VIII.2 involves three different space orbitals, and that it refers to a state for which the resultant spin angular momentum is $+\frac{1}{2} \cdot \frac{h}{2\pi}$ (i.e. the determinant must include two α and one β spin functions). There are three determinants corresponding to this according as β is associated with the first, second or third space orbital. Since it is only possible to distinguish experimentally the *resultant* spin angular momentum, but not which spin orbital is associated with which space orbital, any real state of the system must correspond to a combination of these determinants. This can be illustrated for the two-particle system by the following:

$$\begin{vmatrix} A'(1)\alpha(1) & B'(1)\beta(1) \\ A'(2)\alpha(2) & B'(2)\beta(2) \end{vmatrix} + \begin{vmatrix} A'(1)\beta(1) & B'(1)\alpha(1) \\ A'(2)\beta(2) & B'(2)\alpha(2) \end{vmatrix}$$

$$= \{A'(1)B'(2) - A'(2)B'(1)\}\{\alpha(1)\beta(2) + \alpha(2)\beta(1)\}, \quad \text{(VIII.3)}$$

where A' and B' are space functions. The combination of the determinants with a negative sign is equal to:

$$\{A'(1)B'(2) + A'(2)B'(1)\}\{\alpha(1)\beta(2) - \alpha(2)\beta(1)\}. \quad \text{(VIII.4)}$$

These were the forms that were used in Chapter VI. Therefore the total wave function consists of an array of terms (e.g. VIII.1) which may be represented in some cases by a single determinant, and in others by a combination of determinants. It is this feature that leads to the form of electron spin correlation in many electron systems.

VIII.3 Electronic Energies for Polyelectronic Atoms

In Chapter VI, in addition to examining the ground state of He, four excited states were considered. These were the singlet and triplet states for the orbital occupations $1s2s$ and $1s2p$. It was found that, because of the differences in coulomb energy, the reasons for which were discussed, the $1s2s$ states lay lower on an energy scale than the $1s2p$ states. If the treatment had been extended to $1s3s$, $1s3p$ and $1s3d$ it would have been found that, if the mean energies of the singlet and triplet states had been used to eliminate spin correlation effects, the order of energy would have been: $1s3s$ lowest, $1s3p$ next

I

and $1s3d$ highest. The cause is again the difference in coulomb energies. This pattern of behaviour is encountered for all poly-electronic atomic systems. That is, for a given principal quantum number, the order of energies starting from the lowest is $s, p, d \ldots$ It is this result, together with the operation of the Pauli Principle, that provides the guide to determining which orbitals will be occupied in the ground states of polyelectronic atoms.

For lithium the ground state* is $1s^2 2s$, and the ionisation potential (5·39 eV) smaller than those of H or He. This is because the electron is removed from an orbit having a principal quantum number of 2, and no longer from a $1s$ orbital. Of course, the nuclear charge has become greater than in H or He but, because of the screening by the inner electrons, the effect of the increase in the *effective* nuclear charge is less than that of changing from a shell having a principal quantum number of 1 to a shell having one of 2. The ionisation potential of Be (9·32) is greater because the electron is again removed from a $2s$ orbital, but the nuclear charge has increased. However, for B, with the structure $1s^2 2s^2 2p_{+1}$, it is smaller again (8·30 eV) because an electron in a $2p$ orbital is less tightly bound than one in a $2s$ orbital, and this change has a greater effect than that of increasing the nuclear charge from 4 to 5. Carbon $1s^2 1s^2 2p_{+1} 2p_0$ and nitrogen $1s^2 2s^2 2p_{+1} 2p_0 2p_{-1}$ have the structures they do, because coulomb effects between the electrons are reduced by accommodating the electrons in different $2p$ orbitals. Also the spins of the electrons in the $2p$ orbitals are parallel in the ground states, because of the effects of spin correlation. The ionisation potentials are 11·285 and 14·545 eV. For the ground state of the oxygen atom, the electronic structure is $1s^2 2s^2 2p_{+1}^2 2p_0 2p_{-1}$. Because there are only three $2p$ orbitals, two electrons have to be accommodated in the *same* $2p$ orbital, and this results in an increase in the coulomb repulsion energy. The ionisation potential (13·615 eV) is therefore less than would be expected from an extrapolation of the figures for B, C and N. It is, in fact, less than the ionisation potential of N. The ionisation potentials of F (17·42) and Ne (21·56 eV) are greater, as would be expected. In sodium, because of the Pauli

---

* In this and the following paragraph only the ground states of the atoms are considered.

Principle, the additional electron must be added to the $3s$ orbital and the ionisation potential drops to $5 \cdot 14$ eV (cf. lithium).

The so-called 'building up principle' may be pursued throughout the Periodic Table. Because, at the stage at which the $1s$, $2s$, $2p$, $3s$ and $3p$ are filled, the $4s$ is more tightly bound than the $3d$, the former is filled in K and Ca before the latter takes up any electrons. The filling of the $3d$ shell then accounts for the properties of the elements from Sc to Zn, the first transition series. Similar effects account for the other transition series and for the first and second rare earth series.

However, it must always be remembered that the concept of assigning definite energies to particular orbitals is an approximate one and the variation of coulomb, spin and charge correlation energies with changes in occupation of the orbitals often makes it so approximate that it is misleading. For example the ground state of V is $1s^2 2s^2 2p^6 3s^2 3p^6 3d^3 4s^2$ while that of Cr is $1s^2 2s^2 2p^6 3s^2 3p^6 3d^5 4s$. This cannot be understood on the basis of definite orbital energies. Since the one-electron energy of the $4s$ orbital is lower than that of the $3d$ for an argon-like core, the occupation in V may be regarded as the normal one. On the other hand the coulomb interaction energy of two electrons in a $4s$ orbital operates against this distribution. It appears that in the ground state of chromium this, together with the lowering due to the spin correlation energy, outweighs the difference between the orbital energies so that the structure becomes . . . $3d^5 4s$ instead of . . . $3d^4 4s^2$. Since it is extremely difficult to separate the different effects, and because it is arbitrary to divide the energy into separate parts, it is not possible to predict, in any easy manner, effects such as that observed in chromium. However, it is sometimes possible to use the experimental data as a guide to the relative importance of different factors.

VIII.4 Correlation of Electron Positions

In Chapter VI, Section 6, the way in which the Pauli Principle affected the electron distribution in the singlet and triplet states of He $1s2s$ was described. Because the orbitals have no angular terms, the correlation between the electron positions, which was shown diagrammatically in Figures 10a and 10b, is purely radial. If the wave function involves angular terms, then there may be an angular correlation also.

Consider two electrons, one in an s orbital the other in a p_0 orbital. The wave functions of the singlet and triplet states will be:

$$f_s(r_1).f_p(r_2).\cos\theta_2 + f_s(r_2).f_p(r_1).\cos\theta_1, \qquad \text{(VIII.5)}$$

and

$$f_s(r_1).f_p(r_2).\cos\theta_2 - f_s(r_2).f_p(r_1).\cos\theta_1, \qquad \text{(VIII.6)}$$

where $f_s(r)$ and $f_p(r)$ are the radial functions of the s and p states. If both electrons are at the *same* radius r', VIII.5 and 6 become

$$f_s(r').f_p(r')[\cos\theta_2 + \cos\theta_1], \qquad \text{(VIII.7)}$$

and

$$f_s(r').f_p(r')[\cos\theta_2 - \cos\theta_1]. \qquad \text{(VIII.8)}$$

The square of the first is a maximum when $\theta_1 = \theta_2 = 0$, or $\theta_1 = \theta_2 = \pi$; and the square of the second a maximum when $\theta_1 = 0$ and $\theta_2 = \pi$, or vice versa. Therefore, for configurations in which the electrons are at the same radius, for the singlet state the electrons tend to be on the same side of the nucleus, while, for the triplet (VIII.8), they tend to be on opposite sides. Consequently, if electrons in the different orbitals have a high probability of being at the same distance, or about the same distance, from the nucleus, the configurations of the greatest probability will be with both electrons on the same side of the nucleus for the singlet and on opposite sides for the triplet. If $f_s(r)$ and $f_p(r)$ have maxima at very different radii then there will be high probability of one electron being at small r and one at large r, though still the configuration with them on the same side will be favoured for the singlet, and with them on opposite sides favoured for the triplet.

For the $2p_0$ orbital the configurations of highest probability are on the z axis. Figures 12a and 12b show contour diagrams for configurations in which the electrons are located on the z axis for the singlet and triplet $1s2p_0$ states. It will be seen that there are maxima for configurations in which one electron is at the nucleus, where the $1s$ orbital has its maximum, and one away from the nucleus at the radius, where the $2p$ orbital has its maximum. However, what can also be seen is that, for the singlet state, configurations for which both electrons are on the same side are favoured relative to those for which the electrons are on the opposite side; whereas, for the triplet state, the situation is reversed. If a similar diagram were

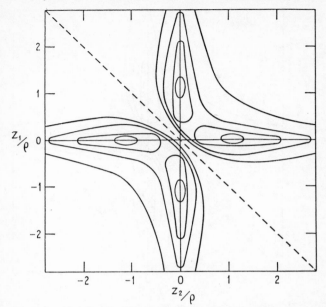

Fig. 12a. Contour diagrams of the wave function of the $1s2p_z$ states of the helium atom, for configurations in which the electrons, 1 and 2, are located on the fixed, z, axis: (a) For ψ_s, singlet.

drawn for the $1s^2 2s 2p$ states of Be for configurations in which two electrons were fixed at the nucleus (the point of highest probability per unit area for the $1s$ orbitals), the same type of behaviour would be found. This provides another example of the tendency of electrons in different orbitals which have opposed spins to come together and of those with the same spin to keep apart. The effect is described most effectively by using hybridised orbitals.

VIII.5 Hybridisation of Atomic Orbitals

Because the permutation (e.g. VIII.1) or determinantal form

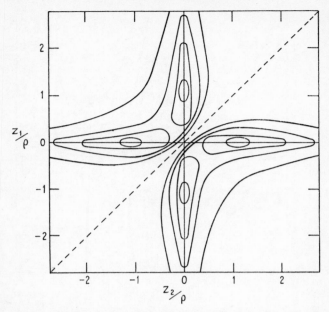

Fig. 12b, (b), For ψ_a, triplet. Nodes are shown by broken lines

(e.g. VIII.2) of the wave function is a combination of a considerable number of terms, it is not easy to estimate the spatial distribution for a many-electron system. This is even true for the two $1s2s$ states of helium. It is not easy to see, at a glance, that the functions VI.34 and VI.35 correspond to the patterns of distribution shown by the contour diagrams in Figure 10a and 10b. However, because of its form, the wave function can be expressed in a variety of different ways. The case of two electrons having parallel spins in the orbitals ψ_A and ψ_B will be studied first. It will be presumed that ψ_A and ψ_B are exact solutions of the single-particle problem, the associated energies being E_A and E_B which are not equal (if they are equal the situation is the special one of degenerate orbitals). Now simple multiplication shows that

$$\frac{1}{\sqrt{2}}[\{a'\psi_A(1) - b'\psi_B(1)\}\{a''\psi_A(2) + b''\psi_B(2)\}$$

$$- \{a'\psi_A(2) - b'\psi_B(2)\}\{a''\psi_A(1) + b''\psi_B(1)\}]$$

$$= \frac{1}{\sqrt{2}}(a'b'' + a''b')\{\psi_A(1)\psi_B(2) - \psi_A(2)\psi_B(1)\}. \quad \text{(VIII.9)}$$

This interesting result shows that the antisymmetric space wave function $\frac{1}{\sqrt{2}}\{\psi_A(1)\psi_B(2) - \psi_A(2)\psi_B(1)\}$ can be replaced with exact equality by a similar formula using another pair of orbitals. If ψ_A and ψ_B were normalised and orthogonal, and the new pair are to be equivalent, then the two new functions must be

$$\cos \alpha . \psi_A(i) - \sin \alpha . \psi_B(i) = H_-(i) \quad \text{(VIII.10)}$$

and
$$\sin \alpha . \psi_A(i) + \cos \alpha . \psi_B(i) = H_+(i). \quad \text{(VIII.11)}$$

In VIII.10 and 11, α can have any value. There are, therefore, an infinite number of forms which can replace the original basic anti-symmetrised wave function. The original description in terms of ψ_A and ψ_B is described as the basic one, because it is expressed in terms of the exact solutions of the single-particle problem. The solution H_- and H_+ are not solutions of the single-electron problem because $E_A \neq E_B$. The functions H_- and H_+ are called *hybrid* orbitals.

The advantage of this process of constructing hybrid orbitals is that, if ψ_A and ψ_B are concentrated in the same region of space, it is often possible to construct hybrids such that one is large in one region while the other is large in another. Take, for example, the $2s2p$ state referred to in the last section in relation to Be. The description in terms of the $2s$ and $2p$ orbitals can be replaced by one using

$$H_- = \frac{1}{\sqrt{2}}(2s - 2p) \quad \text{(VIII.12)}$$

$$H_+ = \frac{1}{\sqrt{2}}(2s + 2p) \quad \text{(VIII.13)}$$

$\left(\alpha \text{ being put equal to } \frac{\pi}{4}\right)$. Figure 13 illustrates diagrammatically the form these hybrids will take. When considering the hydrogen atom,

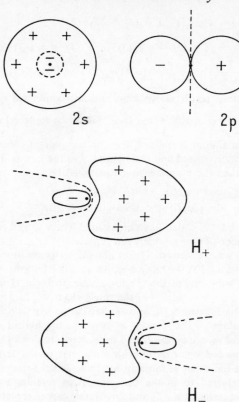

Fig. 13. Diagrammatic representation of

$$H_+ = \frac{1}{\sqrt{2}}(2s + 2p) \text{ and } H_- = \frac{1}{\sqrt{2}}(2s - 2p).$$

Nodes are shown by broken lines

it was found that, for the 2s orbital, the probability of finding the electron outside the spherical nodal surface is greater than finding it inside (cf. Figure 8). Consequently in what follows, our attention will be concentrated on the configurations in which the electrons are not near the nucleus, but on the more probable configurations in which the electrons are in the regions outside the nodal surface. Of the orbitals VIII.12 and VIII.13, H_+ is large in the direction $\theta = 0$, the other is large in the opposite direction $\theta = \pi$. Therefore in the description

$$\frac{1}{\sqrt{2}}\{H_+(1)H_-(2) - H_+(2)H_-(1)\}, \qquad \text{(VIII.14)}$$

if 1 is in the direction $\theta = 0$ and 2 in the direction $\theta = \pi$, the first term will be large and the second small. If the electrons are exchanged the first term will be small and the second large. On the other hand, if both are on the same side both will be small. Hence the description gives a clear representation of the distribution because, in terms of the hybrids H_+ and H_-, the spatial arrangement is rendered apparent. If the orbitals spread over the same region of space, it is not possible to think of one electron being in one orbital and the other in another. Therefore, for the most *effective* representation, α should be chosen in such a way as to concentrate the orbitals H_+ and H_- in different regions of space to as great an extent as possible. Since

$$H_-(1)H_+(2) - H_-(2)H_+(1) = \psi_A(1)\psi_B(2) - \psi_A(2)\psi_B(1), \quad \text{(VIII.15)}$$

it is not possible to say that the former is a 'better' function than the latter. However, it gives a clearer description of the arrangement of the electrons and therefore, for properties which are dependent on the spatial arrangement of the electrons, it is a most useful description and more directly informative than that in terms of ψ_A and ψ_B. But there is nothing fundamental about the hybrid orbitals. What is fundamental is that, if two orbitals are occupied, the position of two electrons in the system correlate with one another, electrons of the same spin tending to keep apart. Hybrid orbitals provide a useful representation of this.

For the case of two electrons with opposed spins in ψ_A and ψ_B,

$$H_+(1)H_+(2) - H_-(1)H_-(2) = \psi_A(1)\psi_B(2) + \psi_A(2)\psi_B(1) \quad \text{(VIII.16)}$$

putting α in VIII.10 and 11 equal to $\dfrac{\pi}{4}$. That is, for this case, only a particular pair of hybrids can be used. For the $2s2p$ state they are those already used (VIII.12 and 13), and the hybrid description corresponds to high probabilities of both being in the region of one hybrid, or both in the region of the other. This brings out clearly the tendency of the two electrons to be on the *same* side of the nucleus.

This construction of hybrids is equivalent to adding and subtracting columns of the determinant (cf. VIII.2 and Appendix III) to and from one another. The procedure can therefore be extended easily and directly to systems involving more than two electrons. For three electrons with the same spin in the orbitals $2s$, $2p_x$ and $2p_y$ a determinantal wave function like VIII.2 can easily be transformed to an equal one made up of the hybrids (often called sp^2 hybrids)

$$H_0 = \frac{1}{\sqrt{3}} 2s + \frac{\sqrt{2}}{\sqrt{3}} 2p_x,$$

$$H_{120} = \frac{1}{\sqrt{3}} 2s - \frac{1}{\sqrt{6}} 2p_x + \frac{1}{\sqrt{2}} 2p_y,$$

$$H_{240} = \frac{1}{\sqrt{3}} 2s - \frac{1}{\sqrt{6}} 2p_x - \frac{1}{\sqrt{2}} 2p_y. \qquad \text{(VIII.17)}$$

These three orbitals are equivalent to one another (i.e. they have the *same form* but they have different orientations). The first is large in the region of the x axis but small elsewhere; the second is large in a direction making 120° with this and the third in the direction making 120° with the other two. That is, they are three equivalent orbitals directed to the corners of an equilateral triangle. They demonstrate that three electrons in these three orbitals, all having the same spin, will have the highest probability of arranging themselves at the corners of an equilateral triangle round the nucleus. The above set of three orbitals is a particular set. There are an infinite number of sets of three equivalent orbitals, directed to the corners of an infinite number of equilateral triangles differently oriented in the xy plane.

If four electrons having the same spin occupy the orbitals $2s$, $2p_x$, $2p_y$ and $2p_z$, the wave function may be transformed to one involving the hybrids:

$$H_1 = \tfrac{1}{2}2s + \tfrac{1}{2}2p_x + \tfrac{1}{2}2p_y + \tfrac{1}{2}2p_z, \qquad \text{(VIII.18)}$$

$$H_2 = \tfrac{1}{2}2s + \tfrac{1}{2}2p_x - \tfrac{1}{2}2p_y - \tfrac{1}{2}2p_z, \qquad \text{(VIII.19)}$$

$$H_3 = \tfrac{1}{2}2s - \tfrac{1}{2}2p_x - \tfrac{1}{2}2p_y + \tfrac{1}{2}2p_z, \qquad \text{(VIII.20)}$$

$$H_4 = \tfrac{1}{2}2s - \tfrac{1}{2}2p_x + \tfrac{1}{2}2p_y - \tfrac{1}{2}2p_z, \qquad \text{(VIII.21)}$$

which have their large values at the corners of a regular tetrahedron round the nucleus. Similarly the group sp^3d^2 (or d^2sp^3) can be converted to a group of six equivalent hybrids, which have their maxima in the directions $+x$, $-x$, $+y$, $-y$, $+z$ and $-z$, showing that six electrons with parallel spin, occupying a set of such orbitals, which have their maximum values at about the same distance from the nucleus, will have a high probability of being at the corners of a regular octahedron.

In all the examples, the descriptions in terms of the orbitals, which were exact for the one-electron problem, were transformed into an equal but alternate description. In Chapter VII the $1s$ orbitals of the hydrogen atom were modified by Dickinson (1933) for H_2^+ and by Rosen (1931) for H_2 by combining a $2p$ type orbital with the $1s$ orbital. This was done in order to polarise each orbital towards the other nucleus. Any other means might have been used to represent the polarisation and, for H_2^+, Guillemin and Zener (1929) did use an alternative way of doing this which was better. This use of hybridisation is different from that which has been described in this section. Rosen and Dickinson used hybridisation to *modify* and *improve* the simple orbital that had been used. The transformation to hybrid orbitals, which has been described in the early part of this section, is a transformation to an *equal* description but to one which shows more clearly the electron distribution as it is affected by spin correlation effects (e.g. the tendency of electrons which have the same spin to keep apart). These two uses of hybridisation are often not clearly distinguished in the literature.

VIII.6 Directed Valency

In Section VIII.4 it was shown that two electrons, with parallel spin, in an s and a p orbital which have maximum values at approximately the same distance from the nucleus, tend to be on opposite sides of the nucleus. Similarly a pair in an s and a pair in a p (i.e. $s^2p^2{}_0$ or $s^2p^2{}_{+1}$) have a tendency, as far as spin correlation is concerned, to group as two close pairs on opposite sides of the nucleus. This is a consequence of electrons of the same spin tending to be apart and those of opposed spins tending to come together. The ion $Hg^=$, if it could exist, would therefore have two pairs on opposite sides of the nucleus and two CH_3^+ groups for example would be bound on opposite sides of the central atom. Thus $Hg(CH_3)_2$ and other covalent compounds of the Group IIB elements such as the dihalides are linear.

By a similar effect the electron spin correlation effects result in $B(CH_3)_3$, BF_3 and the other boron trihalides being triangular and planar.

The electron configuration of highest probability of neon, as far as spin correlation effects are concerned, involves an outer shell of four close pairs at the corners of a regular tetrahedron. The same would be true for C^{4-}. Therefore, when C^{4-} binds to itself four protons it will hold them most strongly if they are at the corners of a regular tetrahedron. The orbitals of the four bonds may be constructed by combining, for each bond, one of the hybrid orbitals with the $1s$ orbital of the adjacent hydrogen atom, in very much the same way as was done for the molecular orbitals of H_2 and H_2^+. As a result four bond orbitals are constructed which are occupied by the four pairs (Linnett and Poë (1951)).

Therefore the reason for the shapes of $Hg(CH_3)_2$, BCl_3 and CH_4 lies in the electron spin correlation effects which have been discussed and, in particular, on the tendency of electrons of like spin to keep apart. This is a fundamental effect arising from the Pauli Principle. It is not dependent on the particular orbitals that are used to describe the system. However, the appropriate hybrid orbitals are the most successful for indicating the spatial distribution of the electrons. If *bond orbitals* are required for these molecules they can be obtained most satisfactorily by combining together, for each bond, one of the hybrid orbitals of the central atom with an orbital belonging to the attached atoms.

The shapes that have been mentioned (equilateral triangle, regular tetrahedron and octahedron), as well as others (trigonal bipyramid), could be explained equally well by the electrostatic charge repulsion of the electron pairs. This correspondence is, of course, not unexpected, because the effect of both like spin, and of like charge, is to keep the electrons apart, and so it follows that the effects will probably be similar. Therefore, broadly speaking, the pairs consist of two electrons of opposed spin which, by the spin correlation effect, are drawn together but, by the charge correlation effect, tend to separate. However, between the pairs, the charge and spin correlation effects operate in the same sense and this probably is an important factor in causing the directional quality of valency bonds to be well defined.

Directed valency will be considered again at the beginning of Chapter X.

VIII.7 Calculations for Many Electron Atoms

The complexity of systems containing many electrons makes any calculation of the wave functions and energies extremely difficult. The difficulty of allowing for r_{12}, in the wave function for a two-electron system, suggests that allowing for many r_{ij} is going to be even more difficult.

Wilson (1933) carried out a treatment of the lithium atom in which he used the independent one-electron orbitals

$$1s(i) = e^{-Z'\frac{r_i}{\rho}}, \tag{VIII.22}$$

and

$$2s(i) = \alpha.\frac{r_i}{\rho}.e^{\frac{-Z''r_i}{2\rho}} - e^{\frac{-Z'''r_i}{2\rho}}. \tag{VIII.23}$$

The energy was minimised at $-14{\cdot}8384$ eV (exptal. $-14{\cdot}9674$ eV; error: $0{\cdot}1290$ eV) with $Z' = 2{\cdot}69$, $Z'' = 1{\cdot}33$, $Z''' = 3{\cdot}0$ and $\alpha = 1{\cdot}34$.

By using the same type of $1s$ function for Li^+ he was able to calculate the ionisation potential. The calculated value was $0{\cdot}3930$ eV (exptal. $0{\cdot}3966$ eV; error $0{\cdot}0036$ eV or 1%). The error in the total energy is forty times the above error in the ionisation potential, so that the accurate value of the ionisation potential must be regarded as rather lucky. The value of Z' is $(3 - 0{\cdot}31)$, which is interesting since it had been found that for He, Li^+, Be^{++}, etc., the best value of Z' for the simplest variation function was $3 - \frac{5}{16} = (3 - 0{\cdot}3125)$ (cf. Section VI.3). The extra electron in the $2s$ orbital, therefore, has very little effect on the *screening constant* ($0{\cdot}31$) of the other $1s$ electron. For the $2s$ orbital the first term is more important when r is large, and the second when r is small. Hence the values of Z'' and Z''' can be understood. The latter is the same as the nuclear charge, while the former is almost two less than the true nuclear charge, the inner $1s$ electrons exerting almost their full screening effect. One might say that each exerts a screening effect of $\frac{1}{2}(3 - 1.33) = 0.835$.

Results like the above led Slater (1930) and Zener (1930) to propose a set of approximate orbitals of the following form:

$$\psi = r^{(n^*-1)} . e^{\frac{-(Z-s)r}{n^*\rho}} . f(\theta, \phi), \qquad \text{(VIII.24)}$$

where n^* may be described as an effective atomic number, and s is a screening constant. Slater and Zener gave a set of rules for choosing n^* and s for particular orbitals. Comparison of VIII.24 with VIII.22 shows that, for the $1s$ orbital, the screening effect of the $2s$ electron is zero, and of the other $1s$ electron 0·31. (The rules of Slater and Zener require 0·30.) For the $2s$ orbital, comparison of VIII.24 with VIII.23 shows that Slater and Zener omitted the second term and that the screening constants for each of the $1s$ electrons was 0·835. (The rules of Slater and Zener require 0·85.) For both VIII.22 and VIII.23 n^* is equal to the true n. The main feature of the Slater–Zener radial wave functions is that all states having $n - l > 1$ are given a single-term function involving $r^{(n^*-1)}$, whereas, for the true hydrogen atom functions, this would be a polynomial in r. The term with the highest power only is included, as this is the most important one when r is large, and the graphs of P_r showed that the electron has the greatest probability of being where this term is the most important. One fault of the Slater–Zener functions is that there is no difference between the radial part of the s, p, d, etc., functions which have the same n. Duncanson and Coulson (1944) gave some improved functions for the first-row elements. These functions of Slater and Zener and of Duncanson and Coulson show the semi-empirical approach to wave mechanics which is one of the ways of attempting to handle very complicated systems. The wave functions are constructed to fit some parameter (e.g. the energy), and they can then be used for other purposes such as the construction of molecular orbitals by linear combination. To that extent, they contribute an attempt to inter-relate a number of properties, the framework of wave mechanics being used to govern the inter-relation.

An interesting way of treating many-electron atoms is that devised by Hartree (1928) and known as the *Self-Consistent Field* method. One first guesses a series of wave functions for the system which contains k electrons, it being supposed that the total wave function is the simple product

$$= \phi_1(1)\phi_2(2)\phi_3(3) \ldots \phi_k(k). \qquad \text{(VIII.25)}$$

Then the potential field for electron 1 in the time average of all the other electrons is calculated. This is given by

$$V_1(r_1, \theta_1, \phi_1) = \int \frac{(\phi_2(2))^2}{r_{12}} d\tau_2 + \int \frac{(\phi_3(3))^2}{r_{13}} d\tau_3 + \ldots$$
$$\int \frac{(\phi_k(k))^2}{r_{1k}} d\tau_k. \qquad \text{(VIII.26)}$$

A new wave function $\phi'_1(1)$ is calculated for electron 1 using the wave equation

$$-\frac{h^2}{8\pi^2 m}\nabla_1^2 \phi'_1(1) - \frac{Ze^2}{r_1}\phi'_1(1) + V_1\phi'_1(1) = E_1\phi'_1(1). \qquad \text{(VIII.27)}$$

This may be carried out on a computing machine. This process can be repeated for $\phi_2(2)$, $\phi_3(3)$ to $\phi_k(k)$ and a new set of functions $\phi'_1(1)$, $\phi'_2(2) \ldots \phi'_k(k)$ obtained. This cycle can be repeated to obtain a third set of functions, and the cycle repeated until there is no significant change in the functions on going through a cycle. The set is then said to be self-consistent. Values are obtained for the energies $E_1 \ldots E_k$, and the self-consistent set of wave functions $\phi_1(1) \ldots \phi_k(k)$ can be used to calculate such quantities as 'form factors' for X-ray scattering.

An objection to the Hartree method is that the function VIII.25 does not involve exchanging the electrons among the orbitals and so does not satisfy the Pauli Principle. Fock (1930) has devised a method which enables this procedure to be applied when the function VIII.25 is replaced by the more correct determinantal form. The disadvantage is, of course, that the calculations are more lengthy.

Boys (1950) has developed a procedure of obtaining atomic wave functions, which is based on the use of e^{-ar^2} instead of e^{-ar} in the trial functions. The advantage of this change is that the integrals obtained are easier to evaluate, and hence it is possible to extend the treatment to more flexible forms for the trial functions.

VIII.8 Orbital Energies in Diatomic Molecules

In section VII.6, the diatomic molecular orbitals were described in terms of the simplest LCAO approximation. These were $\sigma_g 1s$, $\sigma_u 1s$, $\sigma_g 2s$, $\sigma_u 2s$, $\pi_u 2p$, $\pi_g 2p$, etc. The relative energies of these were discussed for H_2^+ and H_2. These orbitals will now be employed in the consideration of diatomic molecules containing more than two electrons. The first problem is to decide the expected order of the orbitals on an energy scale. This will be done for systems in which both nuclei are the same (N_2, O_2, etc.). A guide to this is provided by considering the energies of the orbitals of the separated atoms, and the energies of the orbitals of the united atom (cf. Section VII.6). Because the systems are all polyelectronic, the order may be taken to be $1s$, $2s$, $2p$, $3s$, $3p$, $4s$, $3d$, $4p$ . . . On this basis, the $\sigma_g 1s$ orbital would be expected to be lower than the $\sigma_u 1s$, because they become degenerate in the separated system, but the former goes to $1s$ while the latter goes to $2p$ in the united atom. Similarly the order of the next pair will be $\sigma_g 2s$, $\sigma_u 2s$, since the former goes to $2s$ and the latter to $3p$ in the united atom. The next orbitals of the separated atoms are the $2p$ orbitals. The order of the molecular orbitals derived from these will be expected to be $\pi_u 2p$, $\sigma_g 2p$, $\pi_g 2p$, $\sigma_u 2p$, since they pass in the united atom to $2p$, $3s$, $3d$ and $4p$ respectively. Therefore the order of orbital energies will be expected to be $\sigma_g 1s$, $\sigma_u 1s$, $\sigma_g 2s$, $\sigma_u 2s$, $\pi_u 2p$, $\sigma_g 2p$, $\pi_g 2p$, $\sigma_u 2p$. The 1st, 3rd, 5th and 6th are bonding, since the two atomic orbitals are combined without a nodal plane in the centre, so that there is an increase in electron probability in the bond region. The 2nd, 4th, 7th and 8th are antibonding since the combination involves a central nodal plane, so that the electron probability in the internuclear region is decreased. Also the addition of an extra nodal plane may be expected to result in an increase in the mean kinetic energy. In fact, the general pattern of energies can also be understood on the basis of the number of nodes. The nodes are of two types, which may be described as perpendicular nodal planes (Pn) to which the axis is perpendicular, and nodal planes in which the molecular axis lies. The last will be described as An (axial node). The number and types of the different nodes are: $\sigma_g 1s$, none; $\sigma_u 1s$, one Pn; $\sigma_g 2s$, two, approximately spherical, round the nuclei; $\sigma_u 2s$, two, approximately spherical, round the nuclei, and one Pn; π_u2p, one An; σ_g2p, two Pn; π_g2p, one An and one Pn; σ_u2p, three Pn. This accounts for the order, if an axial node raises the energy more than a perpendicular node, and if the spherical nodes of σ_g2s and σ_u2s are less important. Of course, the consideration of the number of nodes is equivalent to considering the orbitals of the separated atoms which contribute to the molecular orbital, together with the united atom orbital to which the MO passes when the internuclear distance is reduced to zero.

If two helium atoms are brought together, two electrons will occupy the σ_g1s bonding orbital and two the σ_u1s antibonding orbital. As a result, the two atoms do not form a stable molecule for, in addition to the intrinsic bonding or antibonding properties of the orbitals, there is a raising of the energy because of inter-electron repulsion.

If two lithium atoms are brought together there are six electrons. The two electrons in the $2s$ orbitals occupy the σ_g2s bonding orbital (if they have opposed spins). The two pairs in the $1s$ orbitals occupy the σ_g1s and σ_u1s orbitals. However, at the equilibrium separation of Li_2, at which there is a balance between the attraction produced by the electrons in the σ_g2s orbital and the repulsion between the two Li^+ ions, the overlap of the $1s$ orbitals of atoms A and B is small. The result is that they really remain virtually unchanged cores of the two atoms, and the electronic structure of Li_2 can be written as either

$$\sigma_g1s^2.\sigma_u1s^2.\sigma_g2s^2, \quad \text{or} \quad KK.\sigma_g2s^2,$$

where K represents the filled atomic K shell.

Two normal beryllium atoms do not bond for the same reason that two helium atoms do not. The ground state, $KK.\sigma_g2s^2.\sigma_u2s^2$, would produce no resultant bonding.

Two normal boron atoms give a molecule with quite a strong bond (*ca.* 3 eV). The structure is $KK.\sigma_g2s^2.\sigma_u2s^2.\pi_u2p^2$. The ground state is therefore a triplet for the two electrons occupy the separate π-orbitals, which have angular momenta of $+\dfrac{h}{2\pi}$ and $-\dfrac{h}{2\pi}$ about the internuclear axis, and they adopt parallel spins in the lowest state, because of spin correlation effects.

K

134 *Wave Mechanics and Valency*

The ground state of C_2 would be expected to be

$$KK . \sigma_g 2s^2 . \sigma_u 2s^2 . \pi_u 2p^4.$$

For many years it was thought that, in fact, the triplet state

$$KK . \sigma_g 2s^2 . \sigma_u 2s^2 . \pi_u 2p^3 . \sigma_g 2p^1$$

was even lower. However, recently Ballik and Ramsay (1959) have
shown that the former is definitely the lowest, though the difference
between the energies of the two states is extremely small (less than
0·1 eV). It seems that the gain in coulomb and spin correlation
energy, on exciting an electron from the $\pi_u 2p$ to the $\sigma_g 2p$ orbital,
virtually offsets the energy required to transfer the electron to a less
tightly bound orbital. The situation is reminiscent of that encountered with the chromium atom in Section 5.

The ground state of N_2 is $KK . \sigma_g 2s^2 . \sigma_u 2s^2 . \pi_u 2p^4 . \sigma_g 2p^2$, the last six
electrons, since they occupy bonding orbitals constituting the triple
bond. The lowest state of N_2^+ is obtained from N_2 by the removal of
an electron from $\sigma_g 2p$ orbital. This, along with the data for B_2 and
C_2, confirms the order of the $\pi_u 2p$ and $\sigma_g 2p$ orbitals.

The ground state of O_2 is $KK . \sigma_g 2s^2 . \sigma_u 2s^2 . \pi_u 2p^4 . \sigma_g 2p^2 . \pi_g 2p^2$ and,
for the same reason as for B_2, it is a triplet. Therefore this molecular
orbital representation accounts naturally and straightforwardly for
the paramagnetism of O_2 (i.e. the molecule in its ground state has a
magnetic moment resulting from the fact that the spin angular
momenta of the two electrons in the $\pi_g 2p$ orbital add to one another).
Moreover, the bond in O_2 is a double bond since there are six
electrons in the bonding orbitals $\pi_u 2p$ and $\sigma_g 2p$ and two in the antibonding orbital $\pi_g 2p$. The dissociation energy is 5·08 eV. The ground
state of F_2 is a singlet: $KK . \sigma_g 2s^2 . \sigma_u 2s^2 . \pi_u 2p^4 . \sigma_g 2p^2 . \pi_g 2p^4$. The bond
is therefore a single one, since there are two more electrons in bond-
ing than in antibonding orbitals.

The orbitals of heteronuclear molecules may be constructed in
a similar manner but the actual combinations of orbitals depends
on the particular example (i.e. relative nuclear charges). For
molecules in which the nuclear charge is approximately the same
(CO and NO) the results are similar to those for the homonuclear
molecules.

VIII.9 Electron Correlation in Diatomic Molecules

If two helium atoms approach one another the two pairs of electrons pass into the $\sigma_g 1s$ and $\sigma_u 1s$ orbitals. The space wave function for two electrons with parallel spin in these orbitals is

$$\frac{1}{\sqrt{2}} \{\sigma_g 1s(1) . \sigma_u 1s(2) - \sigma_g 1s(2) . \sigma_u 1s(1)\}$$

$$= \frac{1}{\sqrt{2}} \frac{1}{2(1 - S^2)} \{(1s_A(1) + 1s_B(1))(1s_A(2) - 1s_B(2)) - (1s_A(2)$$

$$+ 1s_B(2))(1s_A(1) - 1s_B(1))\}$$

$$= \frac{1}{\sqrt{2}(1 - S^2)} \{1s_A(2) . 1s_B(1) - 1s_A(1) . 1s_B(2)\}. \qquad \text{(VIII.28)}$$

Therefore the system represented in VIII.28 can be described either as two electrons in the bonding and antibonding molecular orbitals, or as one electron in an orbital of atom A and one in an orbital of atom B. Equation VIII.28 shows why there can be no resultant bonding when a pair of corresponding bonding and antibonding orbitals are occupied. Moreover VIII.28 demonstrates an important feature of the repulsion between systems with filled shells (e.g. He and the other inert gas atoms). As the atoms come together the electrons with parallel spin tend to keep apart, and, as a result, the orbitals of the two atoms become more spatially restricted, and this leads to a rise in the electronic kinetic energy. This is added to the coulombic repulsion between the electrons. These two factors contribute to the Van der Waals' repulsion forces.

A second example of electron correlation is that occurring in a bond which contains two bonding electrons, one in a σ and the other in a π bonding orbital. For example the triplet excited state of B_2 ($KK . \sigma_g 2s^2 . \sigma_v 2s^2 . \pi_u 2p . \sigma_g 2p$) would constitute such an example. In a plane drawn normal to the BB axis and bisecting it, the contours of the orbital $\sigma_g 2p$ will be circles round the internuclear axis while the $\pi_u 2p$ orbital will have the usual '*dumb-bell*' contours. The two molecular orbitals can therefore be transformed into two hybrids H_+ and H_-, which are their sum and difference. (This is analogous to the $2s2p$ example considered in Section 4 of this chapter.) The description in terms of the hybrids is equal to the description in terms of the

$\sigma_g 2p$ and $\pi_u 2p$ molecular orbitals. In the bond region, the hybrids have rather the form of bananas, the ends of which are on the boron atoms, one being on one side and the other on the other side of a plane containing the BB axis. Because the hybrids are mainly concentrated in separate regions, they provide a better description of the spatial distribution of the electrons. That is, the most probable configuration is with one electron on one side of the axis and one on the other. This is a consequence of spin correlation and the tendency of electrons of the same spin to keep apart. Thus the $\sigma\pi$ description of the two occupied orbitals may be transformed into a description which is much more reminiscent of the Baeyer description (cf. Chapter IX, Section 1).

The triple bond of nitrogen may be treated in a similar way. The bonding pairs occupy two π orbitals ($\pi_u 2p$) and one σ orbital ($\sigma_g 2p$). Therefore, at the central plane, the distribution of the three orbitals resembles that of the $2s$ and two $2p$ orbitals for boron (except that there is no circular node for the $\sigma_g 2p$). The angular correlation will be the same, the three pairs having their maximum probability at the corners of an equilateral triangle round the internuclear axis. The molecular orbitals can be transformed into three hybrids (using real forms for the $\pi_u 2p$ orbitals):

$$\frac{1}{\sqrt{3}}\sigma_g 2p + \frac{\sqrt{2}}{\sqrt{3}}\pi_u 2p_x, \tag{VIII.29}$$

$$\frac{1}{\sqrt{3}}\sigma_g 2p - \frac{1}{\sqrt{6}}\pi_u 2p_x + \frac{1}{\sqrt{2}}\pi_u 2p_y, \tag{VIII.30}$$

$$\frac{1}{\sqrt{3}}\sigma_g 2p - \frac{1}{\sqrt{6}}\pi_u 2p_x - \frac{1}{\sqrt{2}}\pi_u 2p_y. \tag{VIII.31}$$

There are three equivalent banana-shaped orbitals symmetrically disposed round the axis. They provide a more effective description of the electron distribution in the triple bond than does the $\sigma\pi$ description. The description in terms of these hybrids resembles the Baeyer interpretation of the triple bond. Therefore, although this is a more old-fashioned description, it has advantages compared with the more modern $\sigma\pi$ description as far as spatail distribution is concerned.

VIII.10 Diatomic Molecule Calculations

The molecule Li_2 has been studied by Kotani (1956), the choice of trial functions being based on the principles developed for H_2 (Chapter VII, Section 4). Calculations were carried out for the experimental equilibrium internuclear distance (experimental dissociation energy = 1·03 eV). Using a simple MO treatment, based on $2s$ orbitals, the energy of the molecule was *greater* than that of the separated atoms. By adding $2p$ orbitals in the Dickinson manner a considerable improvement was achieved ($D = 0·075$). However, this was not as good as a Heitler–London treatment based on $2s$ orbitals only ($D = 0·17$). By adding $2p$ orbitals, in the manner of Rosen, a considerable improvement was achieved ($D = 0·30$). Ultimately by using a molecular orbital treatment with configuration interaction, eight configurations being used, D was obtained at 0·764 eV. This treatment can be put in an equivalent Heitler–London-resonance form (cf. Weinbaum for H_2). In all these calculations, Slater-type atomic orbitals were used so that the form of the functions was limited by this. The additional terms in the most complicated function took account of electron correlation, even azimuthal correlation (cf. Hirschfelder and Linnett for H_2), and the tendency of electrons to be drawn into the bond region.

The molecule of N_2 has been treated by Scherr (1955). All fourteen electrons were included individually in the treatment so that the expression used for the potential energy of the system was exact. That is, it did not involve leaving out some of the electrons and then allowing for them in an approximate way. On the other hand the wave functions were constructed as linear combinations of atomic orbitals, the atomic orbitals themselves being approximate. Therefore the forms the wave functions can assume are limited. Moreover, the wave function did not, of course, contain any r_{ij} terms. The calculated total energy was 99·05% of the true value, but the dissociation energy calculated (1·2 eV) was much less than the true value (9·9 eV). It is not really surprising that the dissociation energy is obtained so inaccurately when it is realised that it is only 0·04% of the total energy, and the error in that is 1%. Nitrogen has also been treated as a ten-electron problem (the K electrons being omitted) and a six-electron problem (just the electrons in the $\sigma_u 2p$ and $\pi_g 2p$ orbitals). The values obtained for the dissociation energy are rather better than those obtained using the more complete treatment but this may be accidental. There is necessarily uncertainty attached to the results of a treatment which deals only with a part of the system, and isolates it from the rest in an arbitrary way. Sahni (1953) treated CO in a manner similar to that used by Scherr for nitrogen. He also obtained a total energy which was 99% of the true value (cf. Ransil (1959)). Sahni (1956) also made calculations for BH, and obtained a total energy of -681.8 eV, which was 5.2 eV greater than the true value. The total energy of B + H was calculated to be -680.0, so that the calculated dissociation energy was 1.8 eV, agreeing fairly well with the observed (2.6 eV). However, both these figures are less than the error in the total energy, so that some cancelling of error between B + H and BH has occurred. Boys and Cook (1956) made calculations for BH at three internuclear distances, and obtained a calculated equilibrium length which was exactly the same as the experimental one. The calculated dissociation energy was 1.5 eV. The great merit of the methods and procedures developed by Boys is that they are well suited to the employment of high-speed computing machines.

The results described in this section show that Mulliken's statement (1955) that 'for many years to come the calculation of dissociation energies will prove a hard nut to crack' still remains true.

VIII.11 Conclusion

This chapter has considered many-electron systems. The approximation of independent orbitals has been used throughout. In no treatment of systems of this kind have r_{ij} terms been introduced into the function. Charge correlation effects have been included by configuration interaction (or resonance) or by the self-consistent field procedure developed by Hartree. As was seen with H_2, the success with which configuration interaction or resonance can replace the direct introduction of r_{ij} terms is limited. Consequently the reliable calculations of useful physical quantities for even these simple many-electron systems is not in a very advanced state. Nevertheless the form of the atomic and molecular orbitals, the operation of the Pauli

Principle and correlation effects, etc., set a pattern of behaviour which provides a most valuable background for the examination of such data as ionisation potentials, dissociation energies, etc. It is this that provides one of the most profitable features of the application of wave mechanics to systems the complexity of which makes accurate calculations impossible.

CHAPTER IX

Organic Polyatomic Molecules

IX.1 Introduction

Drastic assumptions have to be made when the methods of the earlier chapters are applied to organic polyatomic molecules. For instance, for benzene, most treatments ignore all electrons except the six of the so-called aromatic sextet. As a consequence many calculations for polyatomic molecules are semi-empirical in character. Their value depends more on providing a pattern for the results than on the calculation of precise numerical values; for example, the relation between two computed quantities is more significant than their absolute values.

IX.2 Molecular Orbitals of Acetylene

The acetylene molecule is linear, HCCH. It will be assumed that the molecular orbitals can be constructed from atomic orbitals. The important atomic orbitals are the hydrogen $1s$ orbitals, the carbon K (or $1s$) orbitals, which will form inner shells as in C_2, and can be omitted from the examination of the valency shells; the $2s$, $2p_z$, $2p_x$ and $2p_y$ orbitals of the carbon atoms. The $2p_x$ and $2p_y$ atomic orbitals will contribute to π molecular orbitals and the rest to σ orbitals (the molecular axis being the z-axis). Let the atoms be labelled H$'$C$'$C$''$H$''$, and let the positive lobes of the carbon $2p_z$ orbitals be directed towards the centre of the molecule. Then the C$'$H$'$ bonding orbital will be approximately

$$\{1s' + a(2s' - 2p_z')\} = \sigma(C'H') \qquad (IX.1)$$

where the hydrogen atom orbital has been combined with the appropriate sp hybrid orbital of C$'$ (cf. Chapter VIII, Section 5). The C$''$H$''$ bonding orbital will be approximately (in this section normalisation constants will be omitted):

$$\{1s'' + a(2s'' - 2p_z'')\} = \sigma(C''H'').$$ (IX.2)

The σ bonding orbital of the $C'C''$ bond will be

$$\{(2s' + 2p_z') + (2s'' + 2p_z'')\} = \sigma_g(CC).$$ (IX.3)

The doubly degenerate π bonding orbitals will be

$$\left.\begin{array}{l}\{2p_x' + 2p_x''\}\\\{2p_y' + 2p_y''\}\end{array}\right\}\pi_u 2p \quad \text{or} \quad \pi_u(CC).$$

(IX.4)
(IX.5)

These five bonding orbitals will accommodate the ten valency electrons of C_2H_2. Each of the five so far listed is associated with a particular bond. The orbitals IX.3, IX.4 and IX.5 are true molecular orbitals in that, for all of them, ψ^2 is the same at equivalent positions in the molecule. The first two, IX.1 and IX.2, can be transformed into the molecular orbitals

$$\{1s' + a(2s' - 2p_z')\} + \{1s'' + a(2s'' - 2p_z'')\} = \sigma_g(CH), \quad \text{(IX.6)}$$

and

$$\{1s' + a(2s' - 2p_z')\} - \{1s'' + a(2s'' - 2p_z'')\} = \sigma_u(CH). \quad \text{(IX.7)}$$

The process of transforming IX.1 and IX.2 into IX.6 and IX.7 is precisely similar to the transformation of the $2s$ and $2p$ into H_+ and H_- in the last chapter (though it more resembles the reverse transformation). Therefore the antisymmetrised determinantal wave function, expressed in terms of IX.6 and IX.7, is exactly equal to that expressed in terms of IX.1 and IX.2. They are alternate forms. However, IX.6 and IX.7 are the molecular orbitals for they have the property that ψ^2 is symmetric to all symmetry operations. As such they are the first approximations to the orbitals that would be solutions of the one-electron problem. These molecular orbitals correspond, for the molecular problem, to the atomic orbitals ($1s, 2s \ldots$) of the atomic problem, except that the latter are exact while the former are approximate. The orbitals IX.1 and IX.2 are bond orbitals and correspond to the hybrids in the atomic problem.

The set of orbitals quoted would be a very first approximation. For example it is not certain that $2p_z$ and $2s$ would occur with equal *weight* in the orbitals IX.2 and IX.3.

Five antibonding orbitals could be constructed in the same way as the above bonding orbitals, by changing signs so that additional nodes were created between the atoms (cf. Chapter VIII).

The electronic structure of the ground state of acetylene in terms of molecular orbitals will therefore be

$$KK \cdot \sigma_g(CH)^2 \cdot \sigma_u(CH)^2 \cdot \sigma_g(CC)^2 \cdot \pi_u(CC)^4. \qquad (IX.8)$$

Ionisation can be described by the removal of one of the electrons giving, say,

$$KK \cdot \sigma_g(CH)^2 \cdot \sigma_u(CH)^2 \cdot \sigma_g(CC)^2 \cdot \pi_u(CC)^3, \qquad (IX.9)$$

while excitation by the absorption of a photon could lead to

$$KK \cdot \sigma_g(CH)^2 \cdot \sigma_u(CH)^2 \cdot \sigma_g(CC)^2 \cdot \pi_u(CC)^3 \cdot \pi_g(CC)^1, \qquad (IX.10)$$

though a linear configuration of the nuclei might not be the most stable one for the electronic structure IX.10.

In N_2 it was shown that the group of orbitals occupied by the six electrons forming the triple bond ($\sigma_g 2p$ and $\pi_u 2p$) could be transformed to three hybrid 'banana-shaped' orbitals. These orbitals showed the tendency of the electrons in the triple bond to have a high probability of being distributed as three pairs round the internuclear axis. The same is true for the orbitals $\sigma_g(CC)$ and $\pi_u(CC)$ of acetylene, so that the triple bond may be visualised more after the Baeyer manner. The pairs of electrons in acetylene, as in methane, tend to be disposed at the corners of a tetrahedron, though, in acetylene, the tetrahedron will not be a regular one. This is a more satisfactory description of the spatial arrangement of the electrons but the MO description (IX.8, IX.9 and IX.10) is more satisfactory for describing ionisation and electronic excitation.

IX.3 Orbitals of Ethylene

In acetylene, the CH bond orbitals were constructed from the hydrogen $1s$ orbitals and sp hybrids of the carbon atoms. In ethylene, the same may be done as a first approximation except that carbon sp^2 hybrids are used. If the four CH bonding orbitals are labelled B_1, B_2, B_3 and B_4 $\left(\begin{matrix} H \diagdown_1 & & _4 \diagup H \\ & \hspace{-1em} {\scriptstyle >} C - C {\scriptstyle <} \\ H \diagup^2 & & ^3 \diagdown H \end{matrix} \right)$, the following molecular orbitals (for which ψ^2 remains unchanged on going from one corresponding point to another in the molecule) may be constructed:

$$B_1 + B_2 + B_3 + B_4 = \psi_{SS}(CH), \qquad (IX.11)$$

$$B_1 + B_2 - B_3 - B_4 = \psi_{SA}(CH), \qquad (IX.12)$$

$$B_1 - B_2 - B_3 + B_4 = \psi_{AS}(CH), \qquad (IX.13)$$

$$B_1 - B_2 + B_3 - B_4 = \psi_{AA}(CH). \qquad (IX.14)$$

There are two planes of symmetry perpendicular to the plane of the molecule. Function IX.11 is symmetric to both planes, IX.14 is antisymmetric to both planes, while the other two are symmetric to one and antisymmetric to the other (but vice versa). These four orbitals will accommodate eight of the valency shell electrons. The remaining four will be in two orbitals associated with the CC bond. One of these will approximate to a σ orbital, and will be formed from the one remaining sp^2 hybrid on each carbon atom. The other will approximate to a π orbital and will be formed by the two $2p_x$ orbitals of each carbon atom (the molecular plane being yz).

The carbon–carbon bond is then a double (four-electron) bond involving an σ orbital and a π orbital. Alternatively the bond might equally well be described in terms of the hybrids $(\sigma + \pi)$ and $(\sigma - \pi)$, which are 'banana-shaped', and interpret the double bond in the Baeyer manner. The σ and π orbitals are the more basic in the sense that they would be satisfactory approximate solutions for one electron present in the field of the six nuclei. They are, as a consequence, suitable for considering electronic excitation or ionisation (cf. acetylene). But the Baeyer-type hybrids describe the electron distribution better and show that, in ethylene also, there is a tetrahedral group of electron pairs round each carbon atom in the most probable configuration. Ethylene is planar because any departure from planarity would tend to take the group of four electron pairs farther away from the regular tetrahedral arrangement.

IX.4 Simple Molecular Orbital Treatment of Butadiene

For this molecule C_4H_6, it will be supposed that there is a set of nine σ bond orbitals (6 CH and 3 CC) holding the framework together in a planar arrangement, and that these account for 18 valency shell electrons. This leaves four electrons to be accommodated in the orbitals for which the molecular plane is a nodal plane. The assumption is made that the molecular orbitals can be represented as a linear combination of the carbon $2p$ orbitals (one from each atom labelled $ABCD$). Suppose one of these electrons is added and that an orbital can be expressed by

$$\psi = C_A 2p_A + C_B 2p_B + C_C 2p_C + C_D 2p_D, \qquad \text{(IX.15)}$$

where $C_A \ldots$ are constants and $2p_A \ldots$ are the orbitals.

Using IX.15 as the variation function one can write, in the usual way, for the mean energy E

$$\int [C_A 2p_A + C_B 2p_B + C_C 2p_C + C_D 2p_D] H [C_A 2p_A + C_B 2p_B$$
$$+ C_C 2p_C + C_D 2p_D]\, d\tau$$
$$= E \int [C_A 2p_A + C_B 2p_B + C_C 2p_C + C_D 2p_D]^2\, d\tau, \qquad \text{(IX.16)}$$

where H is the Hamiltonian. It involves the differential terms, and potential energy terms for the effect of the nuclei, the core electrons, and the electrons in the σ orbitals. Since C_A, C_B, etc., are constants they can be taken outside the integrals, and then the values which will minimise E can be obtained by differentiation, first with respect to C_A and setting $\dfrac{dE}{dC_A}$ equal to zero, then with the respect to C_B and setting $\dfrac{dE}{dC_B}$ equal to zero, and similarly for C_C and C_D. This gives four simultaneous equations which can be used to solve for C_A, etc., and also E. The first of these equations is:

$$C_A[H_{AA} - E S_{AA}] + C_B[H_{AB} - E S_{AB}] + C_C[H_{AC} - E S_{AC}]$$
$$+ C_D[H_{AD} - E S_{AD}] = 0, \qquad \text{(IX.17)}$$

where
$$H_{AA} = \int 2p_A\, H\, 2p_A\, d\tau, \qquad \text{(IX.18)}$$

$$H_{AB} = \int 2p_A\, H\, 2p_B\, d\tau, \quad \text{etc.,} \qquad \text{(IX.19)}$$

$$S_{AA} = \int 2p_A\, 2p_A\, d\tau, \qquad \text{(IX.20)}$$

$$S_{AB} = \int 2p_A\, 2p_B\, d\tau, \quad \text{etc.} \qquad \text{(IX.21)}$$

In the most simple form of this treatment, all overlap integrals involving orbitals on different atoms (S_{AB}, etc.) are put equal to zero. The $2p$ orbitals are normalised, so S_{AA}, etc., are all unity. All the integrals H_{AA}, H_{BB}, etc., are assumed to be the same (α). They measure the energy for removing an electron from a $2p$ atomic orbital, when it is in the potential situation that exists in the molecule. All the integrals H_{AB}, H_{BC}, etc., involving adjacent atoms are assumed to be the same (β). All the integrals H_{AC}, etc., involving non-adjacent atoms are set equal to zero. Though it is illogical to put $S_{AB} = 0$ but $H_{AB} \neq 0$, this is done mainly in the interests of simplifying the treatment. It probably does not affect the pattern of the results, which is perhaps their most important feature. Therefore the four simultaneous equations become

$$(\alpha - E)C_A + \beta C_B = 0, \qquad \text{(IX.22)}$$

$$\beta C_A + (\alpha - E)C_B + \beta C_C = 0, \qquad \text{(IX.23)}$$

$$\beta C_B + (\alpha - E)C_C + \beta C_D = 0, \qquad \text{(IX.24)}$$

$$\beta C_C + (\alpha - E)C_D = 0. \qquad \text{(IX.25)}$$

The theory of equations (cf. Appendix IV) shows that it is only possible to obtain non-zero (i.e. significant) values of C_A, C_B, C_C and C_D if the determinant formed by the coefficients is zero. That is

$$\begin{vmatrix} \alpha - E & \beta & 0 & 0 \\ \beta & \alpha - E & \beta & 0 \\ 0 & \beta & \alpha - E & \beta \\ 0 & 0 & \beta & \alpha - E \end{vmatrix} = 0. \qquad \text{(IX.26)}$$

This reduces to

$$(\alpha - E)^4 - 3\beta^2(\alpha - E)^2 + \beta^4 = 0, \qquad \text{(IX.27)}$$

giving

$$E = \alpha \pm 1\cdot 62\beta \quad \text{and} \quad \alpha \pm 0\cdot 615\beta. \qquad \text{(IX.28)}$$

The integral β is negative because it measures the energy of an electron distribution in the field of the nuclei, core and σ electrons. Therefore the order, as regards energy, of the orbitals is $\alpha + 1\cdot 62\beta$, $\alpha + 0\cdot 615\beta$, $\alpha - 0\cdot 615\beta$, $\alpha - 1\cdot 62\beta$. The four electrons will fill the two lowest orbitals, so that the electronic energy, calculated as the simple sum of orbital energies, is $4\alpha + 4\cdot 47\beta$. A similar treatment of ethylene leads to the determinant:

$$\begin{vmatrix} \alpha - E & \beta \\ \beta & \alpha - E \end{vmatrix} = 0, \qquad \text{(IX.29)}$$

so the two π orbitals have the energies $\alpha + \beta$ and $\alpha - \beta$. Since two electrons will occupy the lower orbital, $(\alpha + \beta)$, the total energy will be $2\alpha + 2\beta$. Therefore the energy of two double bonds is $4\alpha + 4\beta$. Butadiene has a calculated energy $0\cdot47\beta$ lower than this. This may be described as resonance energy (or delocalisation energy) calculated by the molecular orbital method. The lowest excitation energy will involve the transfer of an electron from the orbital of energy $(\alpha + 0\cdot615\beta)$ to the one of energy $(\alpha - 0\cdot615\beta)$. Therefore the excitation energy is $1\cdot23\beta$. Resonance energies and excitation energies in other similar molecules (hexatriene, benzene, naphthalene, etc.) may be calculated in terms of β by the same procedure. The result is that various properties of a number of molecules can be calculated in terms of the single parameter β. It is found that the results do set the resonance energies of a number of molecules in the order they have been found experimentally. That is, the calculations account for the pattern of the data, though the actual numerical values could not have been predicted.

The lowest excitation energy for ethylene is 2β, and for butadiene $1\cdot23\beta$. It would be found that for hexatriene it would be still lower, and would decrease as the length of the conjugated chain increased. That is, the smallest quantum absorbed should decrease and the wave length of the corresponding band increase. This is found to be so and when the conjugated chain becomes long enough the absorption lies in the visible region (e.g. carotenes).

TABLE VII

$\dfrac{E - \alpha}{\beta}$	C_A	C_B	C_C	C_D	$C_A C_B$	$C_B C_C$
$1\cdot62$	$0\cdot372$	$0\cdot602$	$0\cdot602$	$0\cdot372$	$0\cdot224$	$0\cdot362$
$0\cdot615$	$0\cdot602$	$0\cdot372$	$-0\cdot372$	$-0\cdot602$	$0\cdot224$	$-0\cdot138$
$-0\cdot615$	$0\cdot602$	$-0\cdot372$	$-0\cdot372$	$0\cdot602$	$-0\cdot224$	$0\cdot138$
$-1\cdot62$	$0\cdot372$	$-0\cdot602$	$0\cdot602$	$-0\cdot372$	$-0\cdot224$	$-0\cdot362$

In Table VII the values of the constants C_A, C_B . . . are listed for the various orbitals of butadiene. The constants listed in this table are normalised (i.e. $\Sigma\, C_i^2 = 1$ for each state). Coulson (1939) has suggested that the π electron density in the bond ij (i.e. bond order) will be measured by $\Sigma \; C_i C_j$, the summation being for all the electrons involved. Thus for the AB bond in butadiene, the calculated π bond order is $4 \times 0.224 = 0.896$, and for the BC bond it is $(2 \times 0.362 - 2 \times 0.138) = 0.448$. Therefore the total bond order of the bond AB is 1.90, and of the central bond 1.45. (The σ bond is given the order 1.) The observed bond lengths of these two bonds are respectively 1.35 ± 0.02 and 1.46 ± 0.03 Å, which can be compared with the lengths in ethylene (1.34) and ethane (1.54 Å). If the same method is applied to a large number of molecules of this type, the calculated bond orders can be compared with observed lengths for many bonds. It is, in fact, found that this method does account, broadly speaking, for the pattern of the data.

The treatment undoubtedly makes many ruthless assumptions. It supposes that four electrons in the π orbitals can be considered separately, that the field of the electrons in the σ orbitals can be treated as an average effect, that the energy can be calculated as a sum of orbital energies, that exchange and the Pauli Principle can be ignored, that $\Sigma \; C_i C_j$ measures bond order, and that a linear combination of atomic orbitals provides a satisfactory approximation for the molecular orbital. Taking all these together, it is surprising that the method has any success at all. The reason that it does is that it remains strictly empirical, and only attempts to interconnect different items of data. In this it is undoubtedly successful.

IX.5 Simple Molecular Orbital Treatment of Benzene

The benzene molecule may be treated in the same way as butadiene. If this is done, the energies of the six molecular orbitals derived from the six carbon $2p$ orbitals are $\alpha + 2\beta$, $\alpha + \beta$ (twice), $\alpha - \beta$ (twice), $\alpha - 2\beta$. There are two pairs of doubly degenerate levels. The energy of six electrons in the ground state is $6\alpha + 8\beta$. For ethylene (i.e. three double bonds) the energy would be $6\alpha + 6\beta$. Therefore the resonance energy is 2β. This is approximately four times that for butadiene. Experimentally, the resonance energy of benzene is greater than that of butadiene, but the ratio of the 'experimental' values s larger than that calculated.

The normalised coefficients of the various atomic orbitals in the molecular orbitals are set out in Table VIII as was done for butadiene.

Wave Mechanics and Valency

148

TABLE VIII

$\dfrac{E-\alpha}{\beta}$	C_1	C_2	C_3	C_4	C_5	C_6	C_1C_2	C_2C_3	C_3C_4
$+2$	$\dfrac{1}{\sqrt6}$	$\dfrac{1}{\sqrt6}$	$\dfrac{1}{\sqrt6}$	$\dfrac{1}{\sqrt6}$	$\dfrac{1}{\sqrt6}$	$\dfrac{1}{\sqrt6}$	$\dfrac{1}{6}$	$\dfrac{1}{6}$	$\dfrac{1}{6}$
$+1$	0	$\tfrac{1}{2}$	$\tfrac{1}{2}$	0	$-\tfrac{1}{2}$	$-\tfrac{1}{2}$	0	$\tfrac{1}{4}$	0
$+1$	$\dfrac{1}{\sqrt3}$	$\dfrac{1}{2\sqrt3}$	$-\dfrac{1}{2\sqrt3}$	$-\dfrac{1}{\sqrt3}$	$\dfrac{1}{2\sqrt3}$	$\dfrac{1}{2\sqrt3}$	$\dfrac{1}{6}$	$-\dfrac{1}{12}$	$\dfrac{1}{6}$
-1	0	$\tfrac{1}{2}$	$-\tfrac{1}{2}$	0	$\tfrac{1}{2}$	$-\tfrac{1}{2}$	0	$-\tfrac{1}{4}$	0
-1	$\dfrac{1}{\sqrt3}$	$-\dfrac{1}{2\sqrt3}$	$\dfrac{1}{2\sqrt3}$	$\dfrac{1}{\sqrt3}$	$\dfrac{1}{2\sqrt3}$	$-\dfrac{1}{2\sqrt3}$	$-\dfrac{1}{6}$	$\dfrac{1}{12}$	$-\dfrac{1}{6}$
-2	$\dfrac{1}{\sqrt6}$	$-\dfrac{1}{\sqrt6}$	$\dfrac{1}{\sqrt6}$	$\dfrac{1}{\sqrt6}$	$\dfrac{1}{\sqrt6}$	$-\dfrac{1}{\sqrt6}$	$-\dfrac{1}{6}$	$\dfrac{1}{6}$	$-\dfrac{1}{6}$

In this table the atoms are labelled 1 to 6, and two particular pairs have been selected for the degenerate orbitals. Bond orders may be calculated as for butadiene. For bonds 12 and 34 the result is $\{(2 \times \tfrac{1}{6}) + (2 \times \tfrac{1}{6})\} = \tfrac{2}{3}$, and for bond 23 it is

$$\{(2 \times \tfrac{1}{6}) + (2 \times \tfrac{1}{4}) - (2 \times \tfrac{1}{12})\} = \tfrac{2}{3}.$$

The total bond order of each bond is therefore 1·67. This may be compared with bond orders calculated for butadiene. The bond length of 1·38 Å falls, as does the bond order, between the results for the two bonds in butadiene.

This treatment may be extended to polynuclear aromatic hydrocarbons (naphthalene, anthracene, phenanthrene, etc.). The determinants become bigger, but there is no change of principle. The results obtained for relative resonance energies, and for bond orders, are found to be in general agreement with experiment. In naphthalene, as with butadiene, the different bonds have different orders. Using the numbering of the diagram the calculated bond orders are

12, 1·73; 23, 1·60; 56, 1·52; and 61, 1·56. The corresponding experimental bond lengths are 1·365 Å, 1·404, 1·393 and 1·425. In terms of the calculated orders therefore the central bond (5.6) is unexpectedly short. The others fall into the correct order.

IX.6 Simple Molecular Orbital Treatment of Heterocyclic Molecules

This will be illustrated for pyridine. The method is exactly similar, but even in the simplest treatment there are now two values of α, one for C and one for N, and two values of β, one for CN and one for CC. This means that the form of the orbitals is dependent on the values that are selected for $\alpha_N - \alpha_C$ and for β_{CN} in terms of β_{CC}. It is not easy to choose values for these quantities, because it is difficult to assess the consequences of the many assumptions that have been made in setting up the method. However, by empirical arguments, values have been chosen for $\dfrac{(\alpha_N - \alpha_C)}{\beta_{CC}}$ and for $\dfrac{\beta_{CN}}{\beta_{CC}}$ though the values selected by different authors are not always the same. Coulson and Longuet-Higgins (1947) calculated π bond orders of 1·53, 1·70 and 1·64 for the NC_1, C_1C_2 and C_2C_3 bonds round the ring. This method can be extended to other nitrogen and oxygen ring compounds.

IX.7 Reactivities of Conjugated Compounds

Aromatic molecules are most commonly attacked by positively charged species such as $NO_2{}^+$. These might be expected to attack negatively charged centres. Therefore such reagents would be expected to attack most easily centres for which $\Sigma\, C_i{}^2$ (the electron density), summed over all occupied orbitals, is largest. For the benzene molecule this quantity, for atom 1, is

$$\{(2 \times \tfrac{1}{6}) + (2 \times \tfrac{1}{3})\} = 1,$$

and for atom 2, $(2 \times \tfrac{1}{6} + 2 \times \tfrac{1}{4} + 2 \times \tfrac{1}{12}) = 1$. It would be found to be unity for every atom, as would be expected. For the pyridine molecule, however, the values of $\Sigma\, C_i{}^2$ are not uniform. Round the ring, Longuet-Higgins and Coulson (1947) have found them to be N, 1·59; C_1, 0·85; C_2, 0·95 and C_3 (para to N), 0·82. The figure for nitrogen is high, because α_N is bigger than α_C, representing the

L

greater electronegativity of the nitrogen atom resulting from the greater nuclear charge. This drift of electron density to the nitrogen atom causes $\Sigma\ C_i^2$ for all the carbon atoms in pyridine to be less than that for the carbon atoms in benzene. This is consistent with the experimental fact that pyridine nitrates more slowly than benzene. Moreover, the calculated values of electron densities account for the fact that it is nitrated almost exclusively at C_2 (the β carbon atom).

Attack by NH_2^- will be expected to occur more readily than in benzene because the electron densities are uniformly low. This is found to be the case. Attack will be expected to occur where the electron density is lowest; that is at C_1 and C_3 with a preference for C_3. In fact, in the Chichibabin reaction using sodamide, α and γ amino-pyridines are formed though, unexpectedly, the α-compound is the main product.

The above results show that, for pyridine, the calculations account in a general way for the results of attack by anionoid and cationoid reagents. Nevertheless it must be stressed that chemical reactivity is not, strictly speaking, a property of a molecule in its equilibrium configuration. It is a property that depends on the energy and entropy relationship between the initial state and that of a transition complex. Therefore, it is only possible to draw firm conclusions about reactivity if calculations are made for the initial state and a number of transition complexes. This would be laborious and very uncertain, and it does seem likely that the values of relative electron densities will give some measure of the relative ease of reaching transition complexes for attack in the different positions.

It has been suggested that attack by uncharged reagents is likely to be related to the 'free valence'. This may be illustrated for butadiene. For carbon atom A there are three single σ bonds and a π bond of order 0·90; for B there are three single σ bonds and π bonds of order 0·90 and 0·45. Therefore there is more 'free valence' at atom A than at atom B. Hence a reagent like a free alkyl radical may be expected to attack at A rather than at B. This explanation is not altogether convincing. In this case the transition complexes and products really should be considered. For attack by R in the two positions (A and B) the radical products will be

R·CH₂—CH—CH—CH₂   ĊH₂—CH—CH=CH₂.

. . .

            |

           R

     A   *B*

For *A* there is a system of three delocalised electrons spread over three atoms. Such a system will possess resonance or delocalisation energy. For *B* there is a double bond and a free valency at the end carbon atom. For this there is no resonance energy. Therefore the product of attack at *A* will be more stable than that of attack at *B*. The same is likely to be true for the transition complexes, and therefore the energy of activation for attack at *A* will be less than fo attack at *B*.

The calculated electron densities referred to earlier in this section have also been used to assess π electron charge distribution, and hence, what are called π dipole moments. These have been combined with empirical σ bond moments to calculate overall dipole moments. Again some success has been achieved, but the success lies more in the relative moments than in the absolute values.

IX.8 Valence Bond Method

This has not been applied to conjugated and aromatic compounds as widely as has the molecular orbital method. Because the valence bond method was more successful for simple molecules such as H_2 and Li_2, this may seem surprising. The reason is that the molecular orbital method is easier to apply and it leads more naturally to a wider range of calculated quantities which can be compared with experimental data. For example the molecular orbital treatment gives the energies of unoccupied as well as of occupied orbitals and so provides information about electronic excitations. The valence bond method does not do this so easily as a part of the simple initial calculation.

In a valence bond treatment the contributing structures must first be chosen. For instance, for benzene, the two Kékulé and three Dewar structures might be selected. The energy of these is given as a coulomb term (Q) plus an exchange term (J) for each bond, and an exchange term ($-\frac{1}{2}J$) for each adjacent pair of atoms between which there is no π bond (the valence bond method like the MO considers only the six electrons of the aromatic sextet). The energy of a Kékulé form is therefore $Q + 3J - \frac{3}{2}J = Q + \frac{3}{2}J$. The reason why the exchange term for a pair of atoms, between which there is no bond, is $-\frac{1}{2}J$ is the following. The exchange term is $+J$ when the electron spin wave function is antisymmetric (spins opposed). It is $-J$ when it is symmetric (spins parallel). But there are three possibilities of a symmetric spin wave function and only one of an antisymmetric one. Therefore if the electron spins in the two bonds are independent, as is supposed, the chance of them being opposed on adjacent non-bonded atoms is $\frac{1}{4}$ and of being parallel $\frac{3}{4}$. Therefore the exchange term is $\frac{3}{4}(-J) + \frac{1}{4}(+J) = -\frac{1}{2}J$. Suppose that, for a given molecule, two contributing resonance structures A and B can be assumed to be important. The wave function will be approximated by $C_A\psi_A + C_B\psi_B$ and the energy calculated by determinant similar to that derived in a MO treatment. That is,

$$\begin{vmatrix} H_{AA} - S_{AA}E & H_{AB} - S_{AB}E \\ H_{BA} - S_{BA}E & H_{BB} - S_{BB}E \end{vmatrix} = 0 \qquad \text{(IX.30)}$$

where

$$H_{AA} = \int \psi_A H . \psi_A \, d\tau \qquad \text{(IX.31)}$$

$$H_{AB} = \int \psi_A H . \psi_B \, d\tau \qquad \text{(IX.32)}$$

$$S_{AA} = \int \psi_A . \psi_A \, d\tau \qquad \text{(IX.33)}$$

$$S_{AB} = \int \psi_A . \psi_B \, d\tau. \qquad \text{(IX.34)}$$

The argument used in deriving this is exactly the same as for the MO treatment.

The evaluation of the diagonal term for a Kékulé form of benzene has already been considered. It was shown that $(H_{AA} - S_{AA}E)$ is equal to $(Q + \frac{3}{2}J - E)$. The evaluation of the off-diagonal terms is not easy, and it will not be discussed further here except to say that they take the form $(aQ + bJ)$. Therefore the simple valence bond treatment poses the same type of problem as the molecular orbital. What values are to be given to Q and J? Though for homocyclic systems the resonance energy is given in terms of J only, just as the MO resonance energy was given in terms of β only. Therefore, like the MO treatment, this gives directly relative resonance energies. It is found that the order, or pattern, of these resonance energies is very much the same as was predicted by the molecular orbital treatment. Bond orders can be calculated from the weight calculated for the different structures together with the location of the bonds for these structures. However, excitation energies are not provided as satisfactorily as with the molecular orbital treatment. It is true that the determinant IX.30 has two roots, and that while the lower is for the ground state, the upper will be for the excited state. However, this may not be the lowest excited state. Also the valence bond treatment does not, at this initial level of treatment, give anything that can be related to the relative reactivity of different positions in a conjugated chain or ring system.

To summarise, therefore, the simple, valence bond method involves the same type of ruthless assumptions that are involved in the molecular orbital treatment. It has the same semi-empirical character. Moreover it seems that both methods, despite the difference of approach, lead to the same pattern of resonance energies for a range of compounds. Because the simple molecular orbital method yields more information for a given amount of effort it has been used more.

IX.9 Some Improved Methods

Because of the gross simplifications involved in the simple molecular orbital and valence bond treatments of conjugated and aromatic substances, there have been attempts to make improvements and to eliminate at least some of the approximations. It is not possible to examine these in detail. A brief outline of a few of them will be given.

In the simple treatment all overlap integrals, even between orbitals on adjacent atoms, were set equal to zero. There are treatments that have included these. Secondly, the simple treatment regards the electrons as non-interacting, the energy being just a sum of the orbital energies. This has been removed in the so-called self-consistent molecular orbital treatment. In one of these methods the effect, at one atom (i), of the electrons located at another atom (j), was approximated by the potential energy term $\Sigma\ C_j^2 . \dfrac{e^2}{R}$ where $\Sigma\ C_j^2$ is the sum over all occupied orbitals (see earlier). Terms of this type are included for every other atom j. This is done for all atoms in the system and the appropriate terms included in the determinant. At first a set of C_j values must be assumed. The determinant then gives a set of energy levels which give new sets of C_j coefficients. These new C_j values are then included to represent new electron densities on the atoms, and the process repeated to obtain another new set of C_j values. This cycle of processes is repeated until the C_j values remain unaltered. The set of C_j values is then said to be 'self-consistent'. In some ways the choice of the words 'self-consistent' may be regarded as unfortunate. It is true that the procedure bears a formal resemblance to the Hartree method; but it is a very 'watered-down' version. The function used still remains bound by the LCAO approximation, whereas one of the important features of the Hartree treatment was that the atomic orbitals were altered on a much more flexible basis and hence there was much more hope of bringing the treatment nearer to the truth. However, Pritchard and Sumner (1954) have shown that a self-consistent treatment of the above type gives a better account of naphthalene than does the simple molecular orbital one, removing, in particular, the discrepancy that existed regarding the central bond. However, for anthracene, the simple molecular orbital treatment was better than the self-consistent one of Pritchard and Sumner. It is possible to argue that the introduction of an improvement, such as allowing in some way for inter-electron repulsion, is all very well, but so many other major and very unreliable assumptions still remain that one cannot really expect the new version to be any more accurate. Further, it might be said that perhaps, at the moment, all one can do for a molecule of such complexity is to employ a simple treatment and realise that, as yet, only a broad picture of the general behaviour of the systems under consideration can be obtained. Except for the treatment of excited states and electronic excitation it can probably be said that the simple molecular orbital treatment does give an account of the data which is satisfactory in a general way.

Other improvements that have been made to the molecular orbital calculation are the inclusion of σ–π interactions and the addition of configuration interaction with excited configurations in which electrons are excited to the higher orbitals which for the simple ground state configurations are unoccupied. This is analogous to the treatment of Taylor and Parr for helium and, as was said then, is a way of introducing flexibility into the wave function. It provides a standard and routine way of modifying the MO function.

The valence bond treatment can be improved in a similar way; that is, by including resonance with more and more excited structures. In the treatment of the hydrogen molecule, Weinbaum included resonance with ionic structure. Therefore in the more detailed valence bond treatments of benzene, ionic structures derived from both the Kékulé and Dewar structures have been included as well as the simple Kékulé and Dewar forms.

In the simple molecular orbital treatment, the Pauli Principle is ignored and each electron is regarded as occupying a particular orbital. The improvement has been made of employing a fully anti-symmetrised molecular orbital.

Most of these more detailed treatments have been aimed at accounting for ultraviolet absorption spectra. For example that of benzene, in which there are four band systems, has been studied. The interpretation of this spectrum is not completely certain, so the theoretical treatment might be able to aid in the interpretation. The agreement between theory and experiment is not particularly good, though there are certain encouraging features. For example, the most detailed molecular orbital treatment places the lowest triplet level at approximately the correct energy spacing from the ground state. On the other hand, the spacing of the singlet levels is much less satisfactory. A further difficulty over these treatments is that there seems to be little assurance regarding their reliability. It is not infrequently found that the inclusion of an *improvement* produces results which agree less well with experiment (cf. Pritchard and Sumner's calculations of bond orders in anthracene). As was said above, this is not altogether surprising, however, when the ruthless assumptions that remain in even the most involved treatment are remembered. But to allow in any complete way for even some of these assumptions is not possible, because of the prohibitive amount of labour involved. As a consequence there remains a feeling that examples of good numerical agreement may often be a result of good luck rather than of a truly reliable correspondence between theory and experiment. The situation is not encouraging. As regards configuration interaction, Coulson, Craig and Jacobs (1951) suggested that it seemed likely that 'progress in more complicated molecules is not possible in this direction'. Since that time there has been some tendency for theoretical chemists to turn more frequently to simpler systems, such as diatomic molecules, presumably in the hope that, in such systems, it will be possible to obtain results sufficiently close to the true experimental behaviour that worth-while conclusions can be drawn.

IX.10 Conclusion

The applications of wave mechanics in organic chemistry are almost entirely to conjugated and aromatic systems and to the so-called π orbitals of those systems. There have been some studies of the ionisation potentials of aliphatic hydrocarbons, and of induction effects, but the effort that has taken place in these systems is relatively small. It is perhaps not surprising that conjugated and aromatic compounds have attracted most attention, because, as regards the interpretation of reactivity and electronic effects, this was true even before wave mechanics came on the scene. These are exemplified by the various formulae suggested for benzene, by Thiele's partial valencies, by the directing effects for substitution in aromatic systems, and by much other work carried out before 1924.

CHAPTER X

Inorganic Polyatomic Molecules and Ions

X.1 Introduction

The applications of wave mechanics to inorganic compounds are more varied than those to organic compounds. However, in almost all cases they are qualitative. Exceptions to this are the calculations that have been made for simple molecules such as H_2O. Also calculations of a semi-empirical character have been carried out for a variety of complex ions. There have been several methods of approach to the electronic structure of complexes and, in some ways, the extent to which these ions have been examined is comparable to the range of studies that have been made of aromatic compounds. Important qualitative applications of wave mechanics in inorganic chemistry are to the many new compounds which exhibit unexpected valency features. These compounds (boron hydrides, ferrocene, etc.) have formed one of the most interesting branches of chemistry during the last decade. In all cases the abnormal bonding properties have been interpreted in wave mechanical terms. In the following sections, a few example will be selected.

X.2 The Water Molecule

This molecule will be used to show the way in which a fairly accurate attack is made on such a species. Many papers have been published about this molecule, but this account will be restricted to those of Ellison and Shull (1953, 1955), Duncan and Pople (1953), and Boys and Reeves (1956). The experimental data to which the calculations are related are the energy, the dipole moment (1·84 D), the equilibrium inter-bond angle ($104\frac{3}{4}°$) and, to a lesser extent, the force constants.

Ellison and Shull carried out a self-consistent field treatment, based on the approximation that the molecular orbitals could be represented by linear combinations of the $1s$, $2s$ and three $2p$ oxygen atomic orbitals, and the hydrogen $1s$ atomic orbital. Slater atomic functions were used, so that the treatment is limited by restricting it to the LCAO approximation, and by the form of the Slater orbitals. The treatment was self-consistent in a similar sense to that described for benzene, except that the inter-electron repulsion was calculated as an interaction between the charge distributions represented by the orbitals (and not in the simplified manner described for benzene in Chapter IX, Section 8). These electron interactions involved the coefficients of the atomic orbitals in the expressions for the molecular orbitals. Therefore a set of coefficients had to be guessed in order to calculate the terms in the determinant, which was used to obtain the energies and, from them, the coefficients in the expressions for the molecular orbital. A trial and error procedure was used. Eventually the set of coefficients used in the setting up of the determinant was identical (i.e. self-consistent) with the set derived from it.

Ellison and Shull made calculations for a number of internuclear angles (90, 100, 105, 110, 120 and 180°). They carried through two treatments. In the more complete one, they allowed the molecular orbitals to be a mixture of all five atomic orbitals. In the less complete one the oxygen $1s$ orbital was assumed to be unaffected by molecule formation, and the other four (valency shell) orbitals were allowed to mix to form molecular orbitals. Both treatments indicated that the minimum energy was for an angle greater than 120°. For the more complete treatment the calculated total energy was $-2062\cdot5$ eV at 105°, as against the experimental value of $2080\cdot6$ eV. Using the same Slater orbitals to calculate the electronic energy of an oxygen atom, the dissociation energy was calculated to be $7\cdot7$ eV (exptal. $10\cdot06$ eV). The energy calculations are therefore encouraging. The discrepancy in the inter-bond angle is not surprising when the small change of energy with angle (calculated) is realised (100°, $-2062\cdot3$ eV; 110°, $-2062\cdot8$; 120°, $-2063\cdot0$; 180°, $2062\cdot0$). At 105° the calculated electronic energy was $2330\cdot5$ eV, and the nuclear repulsion energy $249\cdot9$ eV. Ellison and Shull calculated the dipole moment as $1\cdot52$ D for 105°, which is in surprisingly good agreement with experiment.

Duncan and Pople carried out a simple molecular orbital treatment for the equilibrium configuration only. They constructed two bond-orbitals from hybrids of oxygen s and p orbitals and the hydrogen $1s$ orbitals, and two equivalent lone-pair orbitals which were also hybrids of s and p orbitals. The coefficients of sp mixing within the hybrids, and of the bonding hybrid with the hydrogen orbital, were chosen to satisfy the inter-bond angle, orthogonality conditions, and the *experimental dipole moment*. It was then possible to compute the various contributions to the electric moment about the oxygen nucleus. The lone pairs contributed $3 \cdot 03$ D, the electrons in the bonding orbitals $-6 \cdot 82$ D, and the protons $5 \cdot 63$ D. Thus the moment of the bonding electrons and protons together is $-1 \cdot 19$ D with the negative end on the hydrogen atoms. This is the reverse of what is concluded from the total moment, for the hydrogen atoms are usually regarded as positive. The resultant of $1 \cdot 84$ is achieved by the large contribution of $3 \cdot 03$ D from the lone-pair electrons, which more than compensates the OH bond moment of $-1 \cdot 19$ D, if it can be so called.

Boys and Reeves have calculated, using a high-speed computer, the energies of H_2O for seven nuclear configurations near the equilibrium one. The calculated equilibrium inter-bond angle is $96°$, and the bond length 5% greater than the observed one. The total calculated energy was $99 \cdot 1\%$ of the experimental one, but the calculated dissociation energy was only just over half the experimental value. Even the force constants have been calculated and agree fairly well with experiment. The procedure used in these calculations is one specially designed for machine calculation.

There have been calculations of similar detail for a few other molecules; for example, for CO_2 by Mulligan (1951), and for O_3 by Fischer-Hjalmars (1955).

X.3 Directed Valency

In Chapter VIII, the triangular arrangement of boron valencies, and the tetrahedral one of carbon valencies, were accounted for in terms of electron correlation, and it was shown that this situation was best described in terms of hybrid orbitals. In the water molecule a similar situation obtains, except that instead of four bonding pairs being disposed tetrahedrally, two lone pairs and two bonding pairs are now disposed in this way. The treatment of Duncan and Pople (1953) emphasised this feature of the electron distribution. In the ammonia molecule also, electron correlation favours a tetrahedral disposition, and so ammonia is pyramidal with inter-bond angles (107°) not very different from that for a regular tetrahedron ($109\frac{1}{2}°$).

This approach may be extended to other molecular and ionic systems. For example, electron correlation favours the trigonal bipyramidal arrangement for five pairs occupying, say, the $3s$, three $3p$, and a $3d$ orbital. As a consequence in PF_5 the fluorine atoms have this arrangement. The molecule SF_4 is isoelectronic as far as the electrons associated with the central atom are concerned. Its shape is therefore based on that of PF_5. One corner of the trigonal bi-pyramid is *occupied* by a lone pair. It would be difficult to predict theoretically whether this would be an equatorial or a polar position; in fact it is an equatorial position. In ClF_3, two equatorial positions are occupied by lone pairs, and the molecule is T-shaped. The ion ClF_2^- would presumably be linear (cf. I_3^-).

Similar arguments may be applied for example to BrF_5, in which the bromine atom is surrounded by six electron pairs in the valency shell and so the structure is based on an octahedral arrangement as in SF_6, only one of the fluorine positions is unoccupied. This is the shape of BrF_5 and of the isoelectronic $SbF_5^=$.

In the series H_2O, H_2S, H_2Se the HAH angle apparently decreases towards 90°. The same is true for NH_3, PH_3, AsH_3, SbH_3. These results were used as an argument for the view that the ideal inter-bond angle was 90° in all these molecules, but that the angle was increased by proton–proton repulsion, the effect being larger the smaller the central atom. The value of 90° was ascribed to the ideal inter-bond angle as being the angle between the lobes of two orthogonal np orbitals ($2p$ in H_2O and NH_3). However, data, such as the vibration frequencies of the water molecule, do not seem to support this interpretation.

An alternative view is to suppose that the 'ideal' angle is the tetrahedral one. In the $O^=$ the four electron pairs will, in their most probable configuration, be mutually disposed at the corners of a tetrahedron because of electron correlation (Chapter VIII). When two protons are brought into this system, they would be bound at $109\frac{1}{2}°$ to one another if there were no distortion of the electron cloud. However, the electron cloud will not remain undistorted, and, in forming the bonding orbitals, the central atom orbitals will be drawn away from the centre towards the protons. Both charge and spin correlation will operate to modify the angular distribution of this distorted tetrahedral arrangement, in such a way that the pairs, for which the average distance from the nucleus is greater, will move closer to one another, while the orbitals associated with the other two pairs (the lone pairs) will spread apart. As a result the inter-bond angle decreases below $109\frac{1}{2}°$. The orbitals for this system will be better described using central atom hybrids which are different from the four equivalent sp^3 hybrids of the regular tetrahedral arrangement. The bonding orbitals will be better described by a hybrid having more p character, and the lone-pair orbitals by hybrids having more s character. This was found by Pople (1953) in his transformation of Ellison and Shull's molecular orbitals to inner, bonding and lone-pair orbitals. Because Ellison and Shull had used a self-consistent treatment, and also an antisymmetrised molecular orbital, they had included some allowance for charge as well as for spin correlation. In H_2S, this distortion of the central atom ($S^=$) orbitals by the protons will be greater, because the atom is larger and the $3s$ and $3p$ orbitals are more polarisable than the $2s$ and $2p$. Consequently, this decrease below the tetrahedral angle will occur to a greater extent, and the description of the bonding orbitals will involve a greater relative contribution from the $3p$ orbital. In H_2Se this effect will be even greater. As a result, as the atomic number of the central atom increases, the central atom contribution to the bonding orbital becomes closer to $2p$ and the inter-bond angle closer to $90°$. The same effect is observed with $NH_3 \ldots SbH_3$.

In fluorine compounds inter-bond angles are surprisingly small. For example, the angle in OF_2 ($102°$) is less than that in H_2O ($104\frac{1}{2}°$); that in NF_3 ($102\frac{1}{2}°$) less than that in NH_3 ($106\frac{3}{4}°$); that in CH_2F_2 ($107°$) less than those in CH_4. By a similar argument to the above this can be ascribed to the high electronegativity of fluorine, and the consequent greater distortion of the central atom orbitals, with the result that a further decrease is produced despite the repulsion between the lone-pair electrons on the fluorine atoms. In ClF_3 the same effect is observed, the FClF angles being less than the ideal value of 90° (cf. $SbF_5^=$ also) (Mellish and Linnett (1954)).

Gillespie and Nyholm (1957) have put this in other words by saying that bonding pairs repel one another less than they repel lone pairs, and the repulsion between lone pairs is greater still. The *repulsion* to which they refer is a genuine electrostatic repulsion as far as charge correlation is concerned, but it represents a Pauli Principle effect as far as spin correlation is concerned.

X.4 Dipole Moments

The interpretation of dipole moments has always been difficult. The moment is the property of the whole molecule and yet, in almost all cases, it is impossible to discuss the charge distribution without dividing it into parts. Such a subdivision must be arbitrary and, in some degree, unsatisfactory. Most experimentalists have used the concept of bond-moments, but this has had only limited success. Moreover, the contributions arising from lone pairs, which are ignored in the simple bond-moment approach, are extremely important as has been seen in the discussion of H_2O in Section 2. In fact, one of the most important contributions of wave mechanics in this field has been that it has led to a realisation of the importance of lone-pair moments.

In hydrogen fluoride a treatment, similar to that outlined for H_2O in Section 2, gives the proton moment, relative to the fluorine nucleus, as 4·4 D. The lone-pair moment is of the order of $2\frac{1}{2}$ D, while the moment arising from the bonding electrons is about -5 D. The situation is therefore similar to that in water. The same is found in NH_3.

The electron distribution in an AB bond orbital can be varied by varying the parameter (λ) which measures the relative contribution of the two atomic orbitals, i.e.

$$\psi_{\text{bond}} = \psi_A + \lambda\psi_B.$$

The molecular orbital type of expression therefore handles the asymmetry of electron distribution in a very simple manner. In the simple valence bond expression:

$$\psi_{\text{bond}} = \psi_A(1).\psi_B(2) + \psi_A(2).\psi_B(1),$$

there is no corresponding parameter. However, in this case an asymmetry of electron distribution can be represented by adding ionic terms (e.g. $\psi_A(1).\psi_A(2)$). If only one ionic term is used then there is one adjustable parameter, as there is for the bond orbital representation, and a corresponding degree of flexibility is achieved. The difference between the two treatments is that the valence bond formula contains no contribution from $\psi_B(1).\psi_B(2)$, while the MO approach includes a contribution which is fixed by λ in relation to the other terms. It is probable that the valence bond formula is closer to the truth, but that the molecular orbital approach has certain technical advantages.

X.5 Boron Hydrides

The simplest boron hydride is B_2H_6, which has a hydrogen bridge structure. Hamilton (1956) has carried out a self-consistent molecular orbital treatment of the central ring system with its four electrons. The eight electrons in the normal (outer) B–H bonds were omitted from the treatment. It was supposed that these bonds were normal sp^2 hybrids $\left(\dfrac{1}{\sqrt{3}}2s + \dfrac{\sqrt{2}}{\sqrt{3}}2p\right)$ and that the residue of the $2s$ and $2p$ boron orbitals were available for the ring. The hydrogen $1s$ orbitals were also available. In the evaluation of the energies and molecular orbitals, Slater atomic orbitals were used, so that the wave function was limited by this, and the assumption about the availability of the boron orbitals. The two occupied orbitals (σ and π) were found to be

$\sigma: 0.190(2s_1 + 2s_2) + 0.268(2p\sigma_1 + 2p\sigma_2) + 0.285(1s_3 + 1s_4),$
$\pi: 0.147(2p\pi_1 + 2p\pi_2) + 0.653(1s_3 - 1s_4).$

In these formulae the boron atoms are labelled 1 and 2 and the hydrogen atoms 3 and 4. These two orbitals represent the σ and π description of the hydrogen bridge (cf. Pitzer's protonated double bond). An alternate description is that the central bond-system can be represented by two three-centre bonds, one involving one hydrogen atom and the other involving the other. The above pair of orbitals can be transformed into an alternate pair (cf. conversion to hybrids), one member not involving $1s_3$ and the other not involving $1s_4$. In these two, the boron orbitals are not directed towards each hydrogen so that the three-centre bond has a somewhat unexpected and irregular shape. However, if a description is given which does use hybrids of the boron atom orbitals which are directed towards the hydrogen atoms, the description is still quite close to that of the self-consistent molecular orbital description derived by Hamilton. It is better than a simple valence bond description involving resonance between one form in which the bonds are between atoms 1 and 3, and 2 and 4, nd another resonance form in which they are between atoms 1 and 4, and 2 and 3. Hamilton concludes, therefore, that the three-centre bond description is better than the resonance description at this level of approximation (cf. Yamazaki (1958)). The treatment could be improved by configuration interaction, or by resonance with more structures.

The other boron hydrides present interesting valency problems which have been examined by Eberhart, Crawford and Lipscomb (1954). Only B_5H_9 will be considered here. The boron atoms are at the corners of a pyramid with a square base. Each boron has a hydrogen atom attached to it by an electron pair bond; and between each pair of adjacent boron atoms in the base of the pyramid there is a bridge hydrogen. Each of these is involved in a three-centre bond. These bonds accommodate nine electron pairs; three pairs remain to bind the apical boron (5) to the four borons (1, 2, 3 and 4) at the base of the pyramid. The orbitals occupied can conveniently be described in the molecular orbital form:

$$(2s_5 + a2p_{z5}) + b(B_1 + B_2 + B_3 + B_4),$$
$$2p_{x5} + c(B_1 - B_3),$$
$$2p_{y5} + c(B_2 - B_4),$$

where B_1, etc., represent the contributing orbitals of the base borons, which probably approximate to tetrahedral hybrids. The symmetry axis of the pyramid is taken to be the z axis and the line joining 1 and 3 is parallel to the x axis and that joining 2 and 4 is parallel to the y axis. In form these resemble the σ and two π orbitals of a triple bond, and they can therefore be replaced by three equivalent hybrids disposed round the axis of the pyramid at 120° to one another. This implies that the apical boron atom will have four pairs arranged in a tetrahedral manner around it. The other borons have the three hydrogen atoms near the corners of a regular tetrahedron, and the apical boron near the fourth tetrahedral direction. The *three* pairs of electrons bind the one boron atom to the *four* others.

The other boron hydrides also necessitate the assumption of three-centre bonds and similar uncommon bonding orbitals. There are also compounds of beryllium, aluminium and gallium which have similar unexpected bond arrangements. These possibilities arise with atoms for which the octet is just under half filled.

X.6 Complex Ions. Molecular Orbital Treatment

There have been three main theories of the electronic structures of these ions. The first was due to Pauling (1938), who considered only the way in which the orbitals of the central atom were occupied. This was very satisfactory for many ions, but there were difficulties in applying it when the number of orbitals available seemed to be too small, either because of the total number of electrons present, or because of the number known to have parallel spin from magnetic susceptibility measurements. In these cases it was supposed either that the ligand electrons made no use of the orbitals of the central atom (Pauling's ionic complexes), or that outer orbitals ($5s$ and $4d$ for elements in the first long period) were used. This approach will not be considered further here. However, it must be stressed that the Pauling interpretation of shape in terms of the orbitals of the central atom that are being used for bonding (d^2sp^3, octahedral; dsp^2, planar, etc.) remains extremely important. It can be interpreted in terms of electron correlation and described in terms of hybrids (Section 3).

In the following discussion more attention will be given to octahedral ions, which are the most common, as the purpose is to illustrate the methods, and not to give a complete account.

For the molecular orbital treatment there are, in the simplest treatment, nine orbitals of the central atom whose contribution is of importance and six of the ligands. For an element in the first long period the central atom orbitals are five $3d$, a $4s$ and three $4p$ orbitals. The six ligand orbitals are the orbitals that are directed towards the central atom; for example, those accommodating the lone pairs in the six NH_3 ligands. It is possible to construct combinations of the ligand orbitals which have the same symmetry as

M

those of the central atom:

$$3d_z : \frac{1}{\sqrt{3}}(L_z + L_{-z}) - \frac{1}{2.\sqrt{3}}(L_x + L_{-x} + L_y + L_{-y}),$$

$$3d_{x^2-y^2} : \frac{1}{2}(L_x + L_{-x} - L_y - L_{-y}),$$

$$4s : \frac{1}{\sqrt{6}}(L_z + L_{-z} + L_x + L_{-x} + L_y + L_{-y}),$$

$$4p_x : \frac{1}{\sqrt{2}}(L_x - L_{-x}),$$

$$4p_y : \frac{1}{\sqrt{2}}(L_y - L_{-y}),$$

$$4p_z : \frac{1}{\sqrt{2}}(L_z - L_{-z}),$$

where L represents a ligand orbital and the ligands are labelled in terms of the cartesian coordinates. There are no combinations of the same symmetry as $3d_{xy}$, $3d_{xz}$, $3d_{yz}$, which, on the simple molecular orbital treatment (without π bonding), remain non-bonding atomic orbitals. The above combinations of ligand orbitals combine with the corresponding central atom orbitals to give six bonding and six antibonding molecular orbitals, according to whether they combine with no additional node, or with additional nodes between the ligands and the central atom (Section VII.6). Using Pauling's cellular type of diagram this situation may be represented as in Figure 14 (Linnett (1959)) (the orbital occupation being that for the ferrifluoride ion).

Single vertical lines separate orbitals that are degenerate, double lines those having different energies.

In *all* stable octahedral ions, the six bonding orbitals are occupied. The occupation of these is equivalent to the six coordinate links from the ligands to the central atom in a valence-bond model. The way in which the other electrons distribute themselves varies, however. For FeF_6^{3-} the distribution is that shown above, but for $Fe(CN)_6^{3-}$ the five electrons not in the bond-orbitals are all accommodated by the non-bonding orbitals and there is only one with an

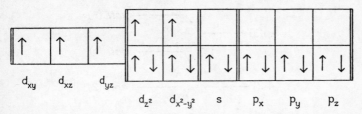

Fig. 14. Pauling-type diagram for representing the occupation of molecular orbitals in FeF_6^{3-}. The antibonding orbitals are set above the corresponding bonding ones, and the non-bonding orbitals are set at a half-way level. Double vertical lines separate levels of different energies; degenerate levels are separated by single vertical lines

unpaired spin. The reason for this lies in the different pattern of orbital energies.

In Figure 15 a diagram of the energy levels is given. This can be linked with the cellular diagram in Figure 14. The actual spacing of the orbitals depends on the relative energies of the different contributing orbitals and their interaction. For fluoride ligands this interaction is small, so that the spacing between the non-bonding and lowest antibonding orbital is small. As a result, the loss in orbital energy in FeF_6^{3-} of putting the five electrons in the separate orbitals, is more than offset by the decrease in coulomb repulsion energy, and the gain in spin correlation energy, because, if they occupy separate orbitals, the electrons can all have parallel spins. On the other hand, in $Fe(CN)_6^{3-}$ the interaction between the ligand and central atom orbitals is much greater so that the spacing between the non-bonding orbitals and the lowest antibonding orbitals is greater. In this ion, the electrons occupy the lowest orbitals they can, because the difference between the orbital energies is large, and therefore the deciding factor. The molecular orbital treatment therefore, explains straightforwardly the difference between the magnetic moments of these ions.

The reason why the interaction of the central atom and ligand orbitals is greater in the cyanide than the fluoride, results from the smaller nuclear charge on the important ligand nucleus (C) in the

M*

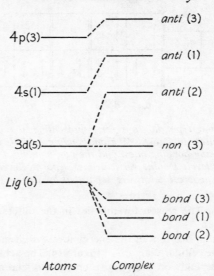

Atoms Complex

Fig. 15. Diagram of energy levels of separate atoms (central and ligand) and of corresponding levels of the octahedral complex showing interrelation: degeneracies are given in brackets

former. As a consequence, the orbital containing the lone-pair electrons is more easily distorted by the field of the positive central ion than in the case of the fluoride. On this basis, it is possible to understand why many complex cyanides and ammines have low magnetic moments (orbital energy spacing large), while aquo-complexes and fluorides have high magnetic moments (orbital energy spacing smaller and correlation energy relatively more important). This also explains a feature of the spectra of these ions which is summarised in Tsuchida's spectrochemical series (1938). The longest wave length band arises from transitions from the highest occupied to the lowest unoccupied orbital. Tsuchida pointed out that for a given central ion the ligands could be placed in an order based on the position of this absorption band; moreover the order was independent of the nature of the central ion. This order is that of the spacing of the non-bonding and antibonding orbitals derived from the central atom $3d$ orbitals. It is found that, in broad outline, the order is based on the sequence halogen, O, N, C. The details for different substances (e.g. ammonia, aliphatic amine, aromatic amine, etc.) are somewhat more difficult to understand.

For such systems it is, of course, virtually impossible to make MO calculations which are really reliable. The difficulties are the same as those encountered in aromatic and conjugated compounds and result from the impossibility of allowing accurately for all the interactions.

In the cobalto-nitrite ion $Co(NO_2)_6^{4-}$, in addition to the occupied bonding orbitals, the non-bonding orbitals will be fully occupied (ligand atom is N) and there will be one electron in the lowest antibonding pair of orbitals. This degenerate pair is derived from one central atom orbital ($3d_{z^2}$) which is concentrated most strongly in the $+z$ and $-z$ directions, and from another ($3d_{x^2-y^2}$) concentrated most strongly in the $+x$, $-x$, $+y$ and $-y$ directions. It can be shown that the electron will occupy one or other of these orbitals and will then exert an antibonding effect in the appropriate directions. Thus, if it occupies the $3d_{z^2}$ antibonding orbital, the bonds in the $+z$ and $-z$ directions will become weaker and the ion will cease to be a regular octahedron. There will be four shorter bonds in a plane and two longer ones at right angles. This is observed in octahedral cupric complexes, for which there are three electrons in the doubly degenerate antibonding pair. The member derived from $3d_{z^2}$ is doubly occupied, and that derived from $3d_{x^2-y^2}$ singly occupied, so that such complexes tend to be essentially planar with two very long bonds at right angles (cf. the structure of $CuSO_4,5H_2O$). This distorting effect, arising from the incomplete occupation of a degenerate group of orbitals, is known as the Jahn–Teller effect.

So far the $3d_{xy}$, $3d_{yz}$, $3d_{xz}$ orbitals have been regarded as non-bonding. Relative to the line from the central atom to the ligands in the x and $-x$ direction the $3d_{xy}$ orbital is of the π-variety. That is, there is a change of sign across the internuclear line. Therefore, with appropriate ligands there can be an interaction between these orbitals and the π-orbitals of the ligands. This type of effect may be important in cyanides (and carbonyls) and increase the bonding of the ligands to the central atom. It may be important also with such ligands as PEt_3, the interaction being between a $3d_{xy}$ orbital of the central ion and a similar orbital on the phosphorus atom, which can act as an acceptor since in the isolated molecule it is unoccupied. The inclusion of such π-interactions will modify the energy diagram in Figure 15.

The treatment of other shapes (planar, tetrahedral, etc.) may be carried out on similar lines.

X.7 Complex Ions. Ligand Field Treatment

Alternatively the effect of the ligands on the orbitals of the central atom may be treated by supposing that the sole effect of the ligands on the central ion is the production of an electric field, there being no orbital interaction of the type considered in the last section. The field will be produced by the octahedral group of lone pairs directed towards the central ion. Because the most important factor in producing the field is an array of *negative* charges the electronic energies of all the central atom orbitals will be raised. However, all five $3d$ orbitals will not be affected in the same way. The $3d_{z^2}$ and $3d_{x^2-y^2}$ orbitals, with *lobes* of high value directed *towards* the ligands, will be more affected than the $3d_{xy}$, $3d_{xz}$, and $3d_{yz}$ orbitals, the *lobes* of which are directed between the principal cartesian axes in which the ligands have been supposed to lie. Therefore the five $3d$ orbitals will be split into a triplet and a doublet, the former having a lower energy. Therefore all the effects considered in the last section which arise from a splitting of the $3d$ orbitals into a triplet and a doublet can be explained, at any rate qualitatively, just as well on the basis of a ligand field treatment. The difference lies in the factors that cause the splitting.

This method has been applied extensively and successfully by Orgel (1952) to chemical problems. For example, he was able to explain the changes in heats of hydration of the ions of the first transition series. The successive electrons are added to the group of $3d$ orbitals. The first three go into the more low-lying triplet, the next two into the doublet, the next three fill up the triplet and the last two fill up the doublet. As a result of the electrons going in alternate groups into the lower-lying set and higher set, there is a periodic change superimposed on the regular increase in the heat of hydration in the series: Ti^{2+}, V^{2+}, Cr^{2+}, . . . Cu^{2+}, Zn^{2+}. This is observed experimentally for the divalent ions, and also for the trivalent ions. Other thermodynamic properties show similar effects (e.g. stability constants). This alternation can, of course, be explained equally well by the molecular orbital treatment, since the explanation is independent of what causes the splitting of the $3d$ orbitals of the central atom.

In the last decade, the application to complex ions of such concepts, together with some semi-empirical calculations, has been one of the most profitable fields of the chemical application of wave mechanics.

X.8 Van der Waals Forces

Van der Waals forces, between say two helium atoms, are of two kinds: those of repulsion and of attraction. The repulsion forces arise because of inter-electron repulsion, and also because of the Pauli Principle, which causes an increase in the kinetic energy of the electrons because of spin correlation between the closed shells as the two atoms come together.

The attraction arises because of a charge correlation between the positions of the electrons. As two helium atoms approach, configurations in which there is a concentration of electronic charge on the same side of the two atoms (i.e. $+ - \ldots + -$) will be favoured relative to configurations in which the electronic charges concentrate on opposite sides of the two atoms (e.g. $+ - \ldots - +$). Since the former configurations correspond to a lowering of the energy by a dipolar type of effect, there will be an attraction between the two systems. This is much smaller than a valency attraction resulting from a resultant movement and concentration of negative charge between the nuclei, and the *closed shell repulsion* operates at larger distances than for systems in which only the inner shells are filled. As a consequence the Van der Waals binding-energy is much less than the valency binding-energy and the minimum in the potential energy curve is at much larger distances.

Because the attraction arises from charge correlation the interaction between three helium atoms will not be the sum of three two-body interactions. The interaction and correlation between one pair will be affected by interaction and correlation with the third atom.

X.9 Conclusion

For inorganic substances wave mechanics has yielded many valuable concepts, and can provide a set of molecular orbitals for the discussion of electronic structures in much the same way as atomic orbitals are employed for atomic structures, the building-up principle being used in combination with the Pauli Principle. However, in most cases, this is more useful in discussing trends in chemical behaviour than in calculating precise numerical values for chemical properties. For only the simplest molecules, such as H_2O, can calculations of such a type be carried through, and even with these, the approximations that have to be made are such that the results are at the present time subject to errors which are large relative to those involved in chemical processes.

CHAPTER XI

Conclusion

Applications of wave mechanics to the physical sciences have been of two kinds. The first are those for which exact solutions are possible. Examples of this are provided by the energy levels of rotating molecules, the simple harmonic oscillator, and the hydrogen atom. The second type of important application is that in which wave mechanics, though unable to furnish an exact treatment, can formulate new ideas, new systems of understanding and fresh inter-relations between experimental data. Applications to electronic structure and valency are essentially all of the second type at the moment, because it has not been possible to treat any electronic system exactly which contains more than one electron. It is true that, by systematic methods of approximation, it is possible to obtain extremely accurate results for the two electron systems He and H_2. For molecular systems containing up to say ten electrons, total energies can be calculated with an accuracy which is usually better than 99%. However, the energies of changes of chemical importance are usually only a very small fraction of the total energy, so that it is not as yet possible to calculate quantities, such as heats of dissociation or energies of activation, with a reliability which is sufficient to make them valuable. Such calculations are still at the point where they are useful as a guide to further development. For molecules containing more electrons than this, it is necessary to deal with some of the electrons only. For instance, in virtually all the calculations that have been made for benzene, 36 of the electrons are ignored and only the six of the aromatic sextet dealt with in the treatments. As a result, it is not possible to assess accurately the potential field in which the six electrons move. Gross approximations have to be made, and most of the treatments are semi-empirical. With complex ions also, the majority of the electrons are left out of the calculations.

In the ligand field method, ten at the most would be considered separately. However, in the conjugated and aromatic systems, in complex ions and the boron hydrides, wave mechanics provides a most valuable means of interpreting chemical trends, even though the performance of exact calculations is out of the question.

When making a critical examination of the treatment of a chemical problem, usually of a molecule, it is necessary first to discover what approximations have been made. This may not always be easy. Then the likely consequences and dangers of the approximations must be estimated. The main difficulty of molecular quantum mechanics is that, for most examples, this is a virtually impossible task even for the most highly expert theoretical chemist. The assumptions are usually so considerable and so intricately interdependent that the consequences cannot be estimated. Therefore it is almost impossible to assess reliability *a priori*.

The assumptions that are made are of two kinds: the limitation of the expression for the potential energy by considering only a part of the system, and the limitation of the type of solution by defining partially the form of the wave function. For instance, in the fourteen-electron treatment of nitrogen, in which each electron is included separately, the expression for the potential energy is exact, but the wave function is restricted to being a combination of atomic orbitals. On the other hand, in any six-electron treatment of benzene, the expression for the potential energy must also be approximate.

In the last few years there has been some tendency to return to the treatment of systems containing fewer than say ten electrons in order that the expression for V shall be exact, and so that the consequences of including approximations can be assessed with greater certainty. For example, the effect of not including the core electrons in the $1s$ orbitals can be examined. In such calculations of physical properties progress is being assisted by the greater use of high-speed computers.

To an increasing extent it is becoming essential to be able to interpret observations in terms of wave mechanics. This is well illustrated by the valency problems that were presented by the discovery of unexpected organo-metallic compounds and the determination of the structure of the boron hydrides.

Appendix I

In this appendix the two-dimensional Schrödinger equation in cartesian coordinates:

$$\frac{\partial^2 \psi}{\partial x^2} + \frac{\partial^2 \psi}{\partial y^2} + \frac{8\pi^2 m}{h^2}(E - V) = 0,$$

will be transformed to the equivalent equation in terms of r and ϕ. The relation between the two sets of coordinates is

$$x = r \cos \phi, \quad \text{and} \quad y = r \sin \phi,$$

and

$$r = (x^2 + y^2)^{\frac{1}{2}}, \quad \text{and} \quad \tan \phi = \frac{y}{x}.$$

Therefore

$$\frac{\partial r}{\partial x} = \frac{1}{2} \cdot \frac{2x}{(x^2 + y^2)^{\frac{1}{2}}} = \frac{x}{r},$$

$$\frac{\partial r}{\partial y} = \frac{y}{r},$$

$$\frac{\partial \phi}{\partial x} = -\cos^2 \phi \, \frac{y}{x^2},$$

and

$$\frac{\partial \phi}{\partial y} = \cos^2 \phi \, \frac{1}{x}.$$

Consequently

$$\frac{\partial \psi}{\partial x} = \frac{\partial \psi}{\partial r} \cdot \frac{\partial r}{\partial x} + \frac{\partial \psi}{\partial \phi} \cdot \frac{\partial \phi}{\partial x}$$

$$= \frac{x}{r} \cdot \frac{\partial \psi}{\partial r} - \cos^2 \phi \, \frac{y}{x^2} \cdot \frac{\partial \psi}{\partial \phi},$$

and

$$\frac{\partial^2 \psi}{\partial x^2} = \frac{x^2}{r^2} \cdot \frac{\partial^2 \psi}{\partial r^2} + \frac{1}{r} \cdot \frac{\partial \psi}{\partial r} - \frac{x^2}{r^3} \cdot \frac{\partial \psi}{\partial r}$$

$$- 2 \sin \phi \cos^3 \phi \, \frac{y^2}{x^4} \cdot \frac{\partial \psi}{\partial \phi} + 2 \cos^2 \phi \, \frac{y}{x^3} \cdot \frac{\partial \psi}{\partial \phi} + \cos^4 \phi \, \frac{y^2}{x^4} \cdot \frac{\partial^2 \psi}{\partial \phi^2}$$

175

$$= \frac{x^2}{r^2} \cdot \frac{\partial^2 \psi}{\partial r^2} + \frac{1}{r} \cdot \frac{\partial \psi}{\partial r} - \frac{x^2}{r^3} \cdot \frac{\partial \psi}{\partial r} - \frac{2 \sin^3 \phi}{\cos \phi} \cdot \frac{1}{r^2} \cdot \frac{\partial \psi}{\partial \phi}$$
$$+ \frac{2 \sin \phi}{\cos \phi} \cdot \frac{1}{r^2} \cdot \frac{\partial \psi}{\partial \phi} + \frac{\sin^2 \phi}{r^2} \cdot \frac{\partial^2 \psi}{\partial \phi^2}.$$

By a similar procedure

$$\frac{\partial^2 \psi}{\partial y^2} = \frac{y^2}{r^2} \cdot \frac{\partial^2 \psi}{\partial r^2} + \frac{1}{r} \cdot \frac{\partial \psi}{\partial r} - \frac{y^2}{r^3} \cdot \frac{\partial \psi}{\partial r} - \frac{2 \sin \phi \cos^2 \phi}{\cos \phi} \cdot \frac{1}{r^2} \cdot \frac{\partial \psi}{\partial \phi} + \frac{\cos^2 \phi}{r^2} \cdot \frac{\partial^2 \psi}{\partial \phi^2}.$$

By addition

$$\frac{\partial^2 \psi}{\partial x^2} + \frac{\partial^2 \psi}{\partial y^2} = \frac{\partial^2 \psi}{\partial r^2} + \frac{1}{r} \cdot \frac{\partial \psi}{\partial r} + \frac{1}{r^2} \cdot \frac{\partial^2 \psi}{\partial \phi^2}.$$

If the particle is restricted to a ring of radius r and there is therefore no variation with r, the Schrödinger equation becomes

$$\frac{1}{r^2} \cdot \frac{d^2 \psi}{d\phi^2} + \frac{8\pi^2 m}{h^2}(E - V)\psi = 0.$$

This was used as equation III.1 in Section III.2.

Appendix II

In this appendix, the three-dimensional Schrödinger equation, expressed in terms of cartesian coordinates, is transformed to the equivalent equation in terms of r, the polar coordinate, for the determination of the spherically symmetrical solutions of the hydrogen atom. (No variation with θ or ϕ.) Now

$$r = (x^2 + y^2 + z^2)^{\frac{1}{2}}.$$

Therefore

$$\frac{\partial r}{\partial x} = \frac{1}{2} \cdot \frac{2x}{(x^2 + y^2 + z^2)^{\frac{1}{2}}} = \frac{x}{r}.$$

Consequently

$$\frac{\partial \psi}{\partial x} = \frac{\partial \psi}{\partial r} \cdot \frac{\partial r}{\partial x} = \frac{x}{r} \cdot \frac{\partial \psi}{\partial r},$$

and

$$\frac{\partial^2 \psi}{\partial x^2} = \frac{x^2}{r^2} \cdot \frac{\partial^2 \psi}{\partial r^2} + \frac{1}{r} \cdot \frac{\partial \psi}{\partial r} - \frac{x^2}{r^3} \cdot \frac{\partial \psi}{\partial r}.$$

Similarly

$$\frac{\partial^2 \psi}{\partial y^2} = \frac{y^2}{r^2} \cdot \frac{\partial^2 \psi}{\partial r^2} + \frac{1}{r} \cdot \frac{\partial \psi}{\partial r} - \frac{y^2}{r^3} \cdot \frac{\partial \psi}{\partial r},$$

and

$$\frac{\partial^2 \psi}{\partial z^2} = \frac{z^2}{r^2} \cdot \frac{\partial^2 \psi}{\partial r^2} + \frac{1}{r} \cdot \frac{\partial \psi}{\partial r} - \frac{z^2}{r^3} \cdot \frac{\partial \psi}{\partial r}.$$

By addition, and remembering that $r^2 = x^2 + y^2 + z^2$,

$$\frac{\partial^2 \psi}{\partial x^2} + \frac{\partial^2 \psi}{\partial y^2} + \frac{\partial^2 \psi}{\partial z^2} = \frac{\partial^2 \psi}{\partial r^2} + \frac{2}{r} \cdot \frac{\partial \psi}{\partial r},$$

and the Schrödinger equation becomes

$$\frac{\partial^2 \psi}{\partial r^2} + \frac{2}{r} \cdot \frac{\partial \psi}{\partial r} + \frac{8\pi^2 m}{h^2}(E - V)\psi = 0.$$

Appendix III

A determinant is written as

$$
\begin{vmatrix}
a_{11} & a_{12} & a_{13} & \cdots \\
a_{21} & a_{22} & a_{23} & \cdots \\
a_{31} & a_{32} & a_{33} & \cdots \\
\cdot & \cdot & \cdot & \\
\cdot & \cdot & \cdot & \\
\cdot & \cdot & \cdot &
\end{vmatrix}.
$$

It is a *shorthand* representation of an algebraic sum of products, there being $\underline{n}$ such products for a determinant of n rows and n columns. Each product term includes one member from each row and one from each column. The main diagonal product ($a_{11}.a_{22}.a_{33}$ ...) is positive. If any other set is written in the order of the rows (i.e. $a_{1i}.a_{2j}.a_{3k}$ ...) then the term is negative if the sequence ijk ... is obtained from $1.2.3$ ... by an odd number of permutations, and positive if it is obtained by an even number of permutations. In a three-row–three-column determinant the signs are

$$
a_{11}.a_{22}.a_{33} - a_{11}.a_{23}.a_{32} + a_{12}.a_{23}.a_{31} - a_{12}.a_{21}.a_{33}
$$
$$
+ a_{13}.a_{21}.a_{32} - a_{13}.a_{22}.a_{31}.
$$

If all the terms in one column, or any multiple of the terms in a column, are added to another column, the value of the determinant is unaffected:

$$
\begin{vmatrix}
a_{11} & a_{12} & a_{13} \\
a_{21} & a_{22} & a_{23} \\
a_{31} & a_{32} & a_{33}
\end{vmatrix}
=
\begin{vmatrix}
a_{11} & (a_{12} + ka_{11}) & a_{13} \\
a_{21} & (a_{22} + ka_{21}) & a_{23} \\
a_{31} & (a_{32} + ka_{31}) & a_{33}
\end{vmatrix}.
$$

The same applies to rows.

If *all* the terms in one column (or row) are zero, the determinant is zero, because every term must include one number from that column (or row).

Appendix IV

The roots of a set of equations

$$a_{11}x_1 + a_{12}x_2 + \ldots + a_{1n}x_n = h_1$$
$$a_{21}x_1 + a_{22}x_2 + \ldots + a_{2n}x_n = h_2$$
$$\vdots \qquad \vdots \qquad \qquad \vdots \qquad \vdots$$
$$a_{n1}x_1 + a_{n2}x_2 + \ldots + a_{nn}x_n = h_n$$

are given by expressions of the form

$$x_1 = \frac{\begin{vmatrix} h_1 & a_{12} & a_{13} & \ldots & a_{1n} \\ h_2 & a_{22} & a_{23} & \ldots & a_{2n} \\ \cdot & \cdot & \cdot & & \cdot \\ \cdot & \cdot & \cdot & & \cdot \\ \cdot & \cdot & \cdot & & \cdot \\ h_n & a_{n2} & a_{n3} & \ldots & a_{nn} \end{vmatrix}}{\begin{vmatrix} a_{11} & a_{12} & a_{13} & \ldots & a_{1n} \\ a_{21} & a_{22} & a_{23} & \ldots & a_{2n} \\ \cdot & \cdot & \cdot & & \cdot \\ \cdot & \cdot & \cdot & & \cdot \\ \cdot & \cdot & \cdot & & \cdot \\ a_{n1} & a_{n2} & a_{n3} & \ldots & a_{nn} \end{vmatrix}}.$$

Therefore, if $h_1 = h_2 = \ldots = h_n = 0$, the determinant in the numerator is zero, and the variables $x_1, x_2 \ldots x_n$ can only be different from zero, if the determinant in the denominator is zero.

Books and Review Articles

Books

Introduction to Quantum Mechanics, by L. PAULING and E. B. WILSON, McGraw-Hill, 1935

Quantum Chemistry, by H. EYRING, J. WALTER and G. E. KIMBALL, Wiley, 1944

Wave Mechanics, by W. HEITLER, O.U.P., 1945

Elements of Wave Mechanics, by N. F. MOTT, C.U.P., 1952

Valence, by C. A. COULSON, O.U.P., 1952

Quantum Chemistry, by K. S. PITZER, Prentice-Hall, 1953

Quantum Chemistry, by W. KAUZMANN, Academic Press, 1957

Review Articles

(a) *Quarterly Reviews of the Chemical Society:*

   C. A. COULSON, 1947, **1**, 144 (General)

   R. D. BROWN, 1952, **6**, 63 (Chapter IX)

   H. C. LONGUET-HIGGINS, 1957, **11**, 121 (Chapter X)

   J. A. POPLE, 1957, **11**, 273 (Chapters VI and VIII)

   J. W. LINNETT and P. G. DICKENS, 1957, **11**, 291 (Chapters VI, VIII, IX, X)

   L. E. ORGEL and J. S. GRIFFITH, 1957, **11**, 381 (Chapter X)

(b) *Annual Review of Physical Chemistry:*

   H. C. LONGUET-HIGGINS and G. W. WHELAND, 1950, **1**, 133 (Chapters VII–X)

   C. A. COULSON, 1952, **3**, 1 (Chapters VII–X)

   J. LENNARD-JONES, 1953, **4**, 167 (Chapters VI, VIII, IX, X)

   A. D. WALSH, 1954, **5**, 163 (Chapters VIII–X)

   R. G. PARR and F. O. ELLISON, 1955, **6**, 171 (Chapters VI–X)

   J. W. LINNETT and P. G. DICKENS, 1957, **8**, 155 (Chapters VI–X)

M. KOTANI, Y. MIZUNO, K. KAYAMA and H. YOSHIZUMI, 1958, **9**, 245 (Chapters VI–X)

(c) Other Review Articles:

L. E. ORGEL, 'Report of the 10th Solvay Council', Brussels, 1956, p. 292 (Chapter X)

J. W. LINNETT, 'Discussions of the Faraday Society', No. 26, 1958, p. 7 (Chapter X)

H. C. LONGUET-HIGGINS, *Adv. in Chemical Physics*, 1958, **1**, 239 (Chapters VI–X)

R. DAUDEL, *Adv. in Chemical Physics*, 1958, **1**, 165 (Chapters IX and X)

PER-OLOV LÖWDIN, *Adv. in Chemical Physics*, 1959, **2**, 207 (Chapters VI–VIII)

G. G. HALL, *Reports on Progress in Physics*, 1959, **22**, 1 (General)

Index